# The
# Supercivilization

## Survival in the Era of
## Human Versus Human

# ESSENTIAL
# CONCEPTS

### John G. Moser, MD

HUMANS *for a* HEALTHIER WORLD
PUBLISHING

NAPA VALLEY, CALIFORNIA

Copyright © 2015 by John G. Moser

Humans for a Healthier World Publishing
1370 Trancas Street #197
Napa, CA 94558
Tel: 855-864-2040        www.healthierworld.us

**Ordering Information**

**Membership Orders.**   As a complimentary part of an annual membership at Humans for a Healthier World, the book is available online at www.healthierworld.us, www.msfh.us, or www.thesupercivilization.us or by calling 855-864-2040.

**Quantity Sales.**   Special discounts are available on quantity purchases by corporations, associations, and others. For more details, contact the Quantity Sales Department at Humans for a Healthier World at the address above.

Tel: 855-864-2040        quantitysales@healthierworld.us

**Individual Sales.**  Humans for a Healthier World publications are available through most bookstores. They can also be ordered through Humans for a Healthier World.

Tel: 855-864-2040        sales@healthierworld.us

**Orders for college textbook/course adoption use.**   Special discounts are available to educational institutions and other nonprofits. Please contact Textbook Sales Department at Humans for a Healthier World at the address above.

Tel: 855-864-2040        textbooksales@healthierworld.us

**Orders by trade bookstores and wholesalers.**   Please contact Bookstore Relations Department at Humans for a Healthier World at the address above.

Tel: 855-864-2040        bookstorerelations@healthierworld.us

Humans for a Healthier World and the Humans for a Healthier World logo are registered trademarks of Humans for a Healthier World, Inc.

Printed in the United States of America

Humans for a Healthier World books are printed on long-lasting acid-free paper. When it is available, we choose paper that has been manufactured by environmentally responsible processes. These may include using trees grown in sustainable forests, incorporating recycled paper, minimizing chlorine in bleaching, or recycling the energy produced at the paper mill.

Publisher's Cataloging-in-Publication data

Moser, John G.
  The Supercivilization : survival in the era of human versus human , essential concepts / by John G. Moser, MD.
    p. cm.
  Includes bibliographical references and index.
    ISBN 978-0-9849398-2-4             978-0-9849398-5-5 (eBook)
    ISBN 978-0-9849398-0-0 (Supercivilization)   978-0-9849398-3-1 (eBook, Supercivilization)
    ISBN 978-0-9849398-1-7 (Abridged)        978-0-9849398-4-8 (eBook, Abridged)

  1. Civilization, Modern --21st century --Forecasting. 2. Disasters --Forecasting. 3. Nature --Effect of human beings on --Forecasting. 4. Climatic changes --Effect of human beings on. 5. World health. 6. Humanity. I. Title.

CB161 .M685 2015
303.49 --dc23                                      2014954182

Book Cover Design: Sara Waters

*To S.M. — We never give up*

# Contents

# List of Figures

# Preface

I began collecting data for this book after my colleague Carolyn Chooljian and I moderated a lecture program in Fresno, California, back in December 2001. The 9/11 attacks had occurred just a few months earlier, and our emergency medicine group held a forum on terrorism in which we discussed what we doctors could do to limit, and treat victims of, terrorist attacks. I soon realized there was nothing we could do if a terrorist truly wanted to destroy America.

I was inspired then to explore stronger global governance (and finally to write the Mission Statement for Humanity and of the inevitability of a global government) after carefully looking at my own profession and the health care industry. I saw a system that was perilously out of control and without centralized leadership. There was no accountability, and every person involved—physician, nurse, health care administrator, pharmaceutical representative, CEO, medical researcher, and patient—was complicit. There was a fear of saying "no." I for one was afraid to speak out due to the fear of losing my job, since as a physician I received the majority of my future salary from a federal government that sets explicit rules of conduct. *Until now*. While there appears to be strong leadership, with the federal government controlling a majority of health care costs, there really isn't. Why? Simply put, the governments of today are not divorced from humanity's most controlling interests; rather, they are the puppets of vested interests who control us. It is within this setting that I began to look at other issues—climate change, illegal immigration, the economic bubbles, terrorism, social pathology, gun violence as of late—and started to realize that this culture of "smaller government" was leading us to an incredible catastrophe.

This book is my attempt to find a fundamental solution to humanity's current predicament—that is, how to deal with shortages in a world with limited resources. I have found that solutions to this particular problem are nearly impossible to implement, given the current social structure and the institutions currently in place. This is true for other major problems of 21st century humanity as well. Solving our health care problem, for example, requires an understanding of the American culture, and to understand the American culture I needed to explore the human predicament. How did we get here? Where are we going? How do we change our course? These questions led to this book.

This essential concepts version was written to assist the reader as a quick reference without detailed theoretical justification. The introduction and twelve chapters are all present (the same as in the theoretical and abridged versions), but they are in an outline format. I have excluded nearly all the endmatter including the notes, bibliography, and glossary but have maintained a sidebar definition of important concepts for quicker understanding. All data is shared between all three versions; no new data is presented in this essential concepts version other than updated data referenced over two years ago (for example, the latest atmospheric $CO_2$ levels). For those readers who would like an extensive presentation of these concepts replete with notes and corresponding bibliography, I suggest they read the theoretical version. Those who want a more concise explanation of the theory may find the abridged version satisfactory. The series bibliography can be viewed online at www.thesupercivilization.us.

## Why Write This Book?

First and foremost, I wrote this book for the sake of humanity. Although that sounds idealistic, even sophomoric, I have waited twelve long years to see fundamental, perhaps even drastic, changes that are necessary for our survival. I have been highly disappointed. I want to save humanity, because like all other humans, I am totally dependent upon the Supercivilization for my survival. I see a significant chance for a major die-off of humanity this century, due primarily to intransigence scripted by individuals who control our thoughts and have no desire to see us make the necessary changes for our survival. There is no alternative, because our imagination is too controlled by our paradigmatic thoughts, which I call the social prion. I don't think our culture currently allows us to see outside of our immediate worldview, and it is up to all of us to break down this barrier and to critically explore our world, starting with a simple question: Why are we not solving those problems that are most likely to lead to our collapse?

Second, I wish to bring the world community together to recognize that we can solve our problems successfully. However, if we remain culturally independent and do not strive to succeed as a Supercivilization, our problem solving will remain ineffective. Cultural differences have, on every objective level, never been more homogeneous, yet we have somehow convinced ourselves that living isolated, culturally distinct lives is perhaps better than homogenizing. I see no alternative but to accept our biosociophysical reality today: we are a Supercivilization. We must start the process of indoctrinating ourselves into the Third Biosociophysical Era and realize that if we don't acknowledge the existence of our Supercivilization, we will succumb to human-induced catastrophe.

## Science

Understanding one's reality using empirical analysis and logic to predict and perhaps even manipulate the future.

## Paradox of scientific execution

In order to study the world, the scientist must remain objective. However, if the scientist is objective, the results of his/her studies must be promoted. In order to promote the results of one's research to benefit society, the scientist must take on those values that his/her research concludes is an accurate description of reality. If a scientist does not promote those conclusions, those conclusions will be lost and scientific advancement will not occur. The objective scientist becomes an *impossibility*. As interconnectedness grows, creating the need for more biological problem solving, the more promotion the scientist must do and the less objective he/she must be. Science breaks down.

Third, and most problematically, I encourage the scientific community to exert its influence in the political realm. Scientists have been aloof and have not stated their views and positions eloquently, forcefully, and with necessary tact. The dissonance between objectivity and science on the one hand and political power on the other has never been greater. Our "most seasoned politicians," Sarah Palin, Rick Perry, and even President Obama have shown "acceptable" ignorance with regard to scientific understanding and advancement. Scientific fact is not a smorgasbord; we cannot pick and choose the facts that are the most compatible with our worldview. Scientific understanding is our reality, and the sooner our leaders accept that science is what it is and not what they want it to be, the sooner we can solve our most monumentally difficult problems.

There is one major problem with the objective, detached scientist today: a scientist studying his or her own demise cannot remain objective. If you die as a human being, you die as a scientist too. Our biggest problem today is translating scientific understanding to the political realm in order to sustain our standard of living. That requires values, and scientists who promote objectivity are inherently burdened by this paradox of scientific execution. How can one objectively study anything when merely selecting what is to be studied unavoidably demonstrates prima facie bias? In this Third Biosociophysical Era, as I will point out, this task becomes far more difficult as the horrific thundercloud of vested interests descends upon humanity.

# Acknowledgments

I wish to give thanks to the many people who have made this twelve-year project possible. I start with Tom Utecht, MD, who was the first person to read the first draft of the book and tell me I wasn't crazy for writing it. The individuals who helped with the research and served as critical readers include Joshua Champion, Yuewen Ding, Michelle Hwang, Owen Kemp, Jaclyn Leong, Alex Mankovich, Bianca Rodriguez, and Gabriel Rodriguez. I give special thanks to Sara Waters as our graphic designer; Marla Wilson as our editor, indexer, and project manager; Hae Yuon Kim as our designer; Rich Conti as our printing liaison; Andrew Campion, who was a major critical reader and leading research assistant; Noah Lee, who was our initial lead researcher; Jacob Loeffler as our final research assistant; and Joshua Hernandez as our website creator. Karen Frank, JD, at Coblentz, Patch, Duffy, & Bass helped with our legal questions. Peg Booth and Julia Wouk of Booth Media Group helped with the marketing.

I would also like to credit the individuals, none of whom I have ever met, whose writings directly inspired this book. They are my teachers. These individuals who served as a foundation for the book are, in descending order of importance: Jared Diamond, whose writings have reached out to all humans by presenting complex scientific concepts in the most artistic and efficient way, making scientists seem human and showing how individual differences are magnified by the unique circumstances each individual faces; Thomas Kuhn, who first revealed how science is not without its massive waves of change and how subtle forces forever eliminate the possibility of the truly objective scientific endeavor; Steven Lukes (whom I first read in the 1980s while I was an undergraduate at Berkeley), whose writings presented his own and Foucaultian concepts that focus on methods for controlling others; Robert Axelrod, who showed that cooperation is not only possible but necessary for our survival; Max Weber, who has demonstrated that historical determinism is not the most valuable concept; Émile Durkheim, who showed the importance of functionalism before functionalism became socially mandatory; Karl Popper and George Soros, for presenting an antihistoricist stance and allowing individuals to see the important difference between biological and physical scientific concepts; Karl Marx, who revealed the shortcomings of capitalism and first showed the power that vested interests can have over the rest of society and its institutions, particularly the state; Paul Ehrlich, who was the bravest of all, writing about controversial concepts—including humanity's senseless misuse of our resource base—before doing so was popular; Albert Gore, for so effectively teaching me and all humans about climate change; Carl Sagan, who postulated that humans are not the central feature of a vast universe; Thomas Homer-Dixon, for critically evaluating our current scientific shortfalls in a highly unpredictable world; Ernst Mayr, for brilliantly laying out biological complexity and showing how little we truly know about biological organisms and how to study them; Richard Dawkins, for constantly questioning our cultural values and  the function and purpose of religion; René Dubos, for acknowledging that the best way to apply medical knowledge is not to treat the ill retrospectively through medicine but rather to prospectively change culture to eliminate our public health ills; Stanton Peele, for acknowledging that the disease state is entirely subjective;  Jeffrey Sachs, for searching for real solutions to the problems of humanity, especially in the Third World; and John Robb, who has brilliantly detailed the potential social pathology that exists in the twenty-first century and the reasons that current nation-states and previous methods of fighting terrorists are now devolving in significance.

"Reality seems valueless by comparison to the dreams of fevered imaginations; reality is therefore abandoned."

—Émile Durkheim
(1858–1917), the father of the organismal and functional view of society and father of modern sociology

# Introduction

"Extraordinary times call for extraordinary measures."

*—Ben Bernanke, chairman of the*
*Federal Reserve System's Board of Governors, 2009*

# Realistic Possibility of Humanity's Complete Self-Annihilation

Unlike previous periods of human history, humankind is now faced with the realistic possibility of self-annihilation. We must immediately reduce our chances of this event happening. We have yet to make a serious, concerted attempt to reduce this possibility. The most challenging aspect of saving humanity from itself is as follows:

- Technological developments, although important, are the least critical.

- Scientific understanding of our universe, its laws, and human behavior, although important, is not critical.

- Our sociological and political structure is by far the most critical aspect to our success, because it determines what we study, which problems we resolve, and where we put our resources and efforts.

# Why Don't We Resolve Obvious Overarching Problems?

Our most serious problems are not being resolved. Most likely climate change will be our greatest challenge in the history of humanity, but we ignore it. Other problems such as health care languish to the point of a slow, painful drain on resources. On the one hand, we will make a priority or even go to war over other issues of less critical nature, such as that of the September 11 attacks and terrorism. Climate change is the elephant in the room, yet we find so many reasons to convince ourselves it is not a major threat. As far as resolving problems caused by climate change, we have yet to declare war on $CO_2$. Why? Why are we in denial?

Those who control the world's agenda will control our fate. It is important for all of us—not minority interests—to control the world's agenda. I fear that leadership intransigence will make self-annihilation more likely, because cultural differences will create more social unrest, which, in a highly interconnected world, spells disaster. How do we fight this intransigence?

- We must appropriately decide (or triage) which of these problems are worth solving. We haven't.

- The key to our survival is our perceptions of who we are, as the problems we choose to resolve reflect our cohesiveness. We often solve irrelevant, meaningless problems with pseudosolutions that benefit only the small minority who control the world's agenda.

- We must solve the problems that need resolving to benefit all of humanity. Until we create stronger world leadership willing to confront minority interests who maintain the status quo, we are destined for catastrophe.

## Biosociophysical Eras of Humanity

The Biosociophysical Eras of Humanity are critical for us to acknowledge and understand because they reflect the current need to create cohesion, coordination, and cooperation in an ever increasingly splintered world. This splintering is creating massive threats to our existence as a result of the rise of technology, increased interconnectedness, increased disparity in wealth, and a declining resource base.

- **First Biosociophysical Era (Pre-10,000 BC):** Nature primarily determined our fate (we didn't understand physical and biological forces)

- **Second Biosociophysical Era (10,000 BC to AD 2000):** Nature and humans determined our fate (biological, sociological, and physical forces)

- **Third Biosociophysical Era (Post-AD 2000):** Humans determine our fate (primarily sociological forces)

## The Supercivilization

This describes the interconnected world of humanity beginning around AD 2000. We are one primary culture with one essential set of social norms and values. We have for the first time become a de facto single civilization with the following three primarily unique characteristics:

- The interconnectedness (ICQ/ITQ; see page 21) is exponentially greater than at any other time in human history.

- The disparity in wealth is more massive and transparent than at any time in history.

- The resource base is critically unsustainable for our relative standard of living.

To successfully and efficiently implement solutions to our global problems, we must acknowledge the existence of the Supercivilization and understand how critical it is to live cooperatively, not competitively.

# Purpose of the Mission Statement for Humanity

Because of our biosociophysical reality today, we must now choose between saving individual humans or saving humanity. We have not decided, but if we choose the former and not the latter, we are destined for a die-off of historic proportions. The Mission Statement for Humanity is a ten-point commitment designed to respond to our current Supercivilization-threatening challenges. The goals of the Mission Statement are as follows:

- Focus humanity on our main challenge today: ourselves.

- Foster unprecedented coordination and cooperation between all 7 billion people in the world to save all of us from self-annihilation.

- Protect us from ourselves—from terrorists, from rogue leaders and institutions (such as rogue governments without fundamental constitutional protections and civil rights), and from anyone or any group that does not have humanity's best interest in mind.

- It is essential we encourage all of humanity (all 7 billion, **excluding no one**) sign this Mission Statement and adhere to its philosophy of group survival.

## Pseudosolutions

Solutions to problems from which small, vested interests receive the benefits, while humanity as a whole derives little, if any, benefit. Pseudosolutions are damaging in two ways: they distract us from other more critical and real problems for humanity; the expenditures for the solution often exceed the cost of the problem itself.

## Biosociophysical Eras of Humanity

Biosociophysical (**bio**logical, **socio**logical, **physical**) eras: periods in which humanity's greatest challenges are categorized by cause—the biosociophysical forces which determine our fates as individuals and as a species.

## Interconnectedness

A measure of how close all individuals are to one another in a given society, civiilization, species, or arbitrary geographical area. It is measured in two ways: by the Interconnectedness Communication Quotient (ICQ) and the Interconnectedness Transportation Quotient (ITQ).

# Mission Statement for Humanity

I encourage humanity to universally adopt the following ten points not only to preserve our current standard of living throughout the twenty-first century but also to promote the survival of humankind in its entirety.

1. **Create a liberal democracy-based global government** (with powers similar to and modeled after those laid out in the United States Constitution, with a federalist concept and a full Bill of Rights) that will (a) create unanimous support for much-needed globally based initiatives and (b) procure resources that will be used to create less susceptibility to rogue humankind destruction (whether through immediate annihilation or slow demise) and discourage rogue behavior (both institutional and individual) through adequate enforcement by all the world's countries.

2. **Encourage comprehensive, unanimous cooperation** rather than competition or conflict to resolve humanity's most threatening problems. Carefully controlled competition with strict governmental oversight and well-defined, transparent, universal rules of conduct will maximize production of goods and services while minimizing (a) environmental destruction, (b) misuse of the world's synthetic and natural resources, and (c) gross disparities in personal wealth.

3. **Maintain complete enfranchisement of all humans** over the age of 17 with complete voting rights regardless of race, ethnicity, gender, class, or geographical origin. One human adult equals one vote. In promoting this egalitarian global government, I advocate minimizing undue influence from special interests by limiting all campaign contributions to prespecified amounts ($1,000 per individual contributor annually). Contributions can only be made by individuals and not by entities such as corporations and unions. Contributions must be limited in order to (a) safeguard the fertile development of only the most beneficial ideas for all of humankind and (b) discourage the promotion of obfuscating ideology for the express benefit of the most advantaged individuals.

4. **Promote better human and global health** and instill these values in all human beings. I advocate a fourth branch of government based upon the World Health Organization model and designed to promote human health independently of the other three branches.

5. **Human health and global health are fundamentally integrated concepts**, and neither can be successful without the success of both.

6. **Educate individuals about evidence-based concepts** relating to human and global health.

7. **Promote zero population growth for humanity** in the twenty-first century by (a) improving the living standards in less developed countries and (b) encouraging migration patterns that would promote better economics for all humans. By encouraging poor areas with young populations to provide a workforce for the older, wealthier areas of the world, we limit vicious poverty traps that encourage procreation to become a viable but dangerous alternative. For both developed and developing areas that have fewer local opportunities for those living in isolation, this melting pot will give all of humanity less incentive to procreate their way to further their own wealth.

8. **Encourage individuals to think critically** about resource utilization and their own health and to realize that the two concepts are fundamentally linked.

9. **Promote better utilization** of existing resources.

10. **Promote adequate and sufficient resource allocation** by all the world's countries to maintain optimal global and human health so that humankind can see universal improvement in living standards. Higher living standards by all individuals throughout the world will in and of itself discourage rogue behavior by individuals and institutions.

# Need for a Global Government

The concept of a world government is not new. Starting with Immanuel Kant, a world government has been debated, but has never been seriously considered. Among those who have favored stronger global governance:

Albert Einstein

Wendell Willkie

Mahatma Ghandi

Bertrand Russell

Winston Churchill

Alexander Wendt

Norman Cousins

World Federalist Association

World Constitution and Parliament Association

Ulysses S. Grant

Alan Cranston

# Six Steps to Protect Us All From Self-Annihilation

In order to save us from ourselves and minimize (never totally eliminate) the possibility of self-annihilation, we need to accomplish six steps. None have been accomplished yet.

1. **Global realization:** We must realize our biosociophysical reality and our own threat to ourselves.

2. **Identify the pathology:** We must identify that the most critical pathology we face is ourselves. We must remain focused and avoid distractions from lesser pathologies that have little relevance.

3. **Understand the pathology:** We must understand our problems and direct appropriate resources to their study. This requires coordinated research studies.

## Climate change

The Intergovernmental Panel on Climate Change officially recognized climate change in 2013 (Fifth Assessment Report at http://www.ipcc.ch/report/ar5/wg1/) as being "extremely likely" to be caused by humans. Greenhouse gases, such as carbon dioxide and methane, have created a human-induced warming of the Earth's atmosphere of almost 1° C over the last 120 years.

## 2040

This is the self-imposed deadline by which we should seek universal acknowledgment of the existence of the Supercivilization. If universal cooperation is not achieved, especially to resolve climate change and the threat of a self-perpetuating greenhouse effect, a synergistic catastrophe such as a Class VIII Event (see pages 92 and 93) could move from a possibility to a probability. It is at this point that we will be left with a critically difficult decision: saving humanity or saving ourselves.

4. **Unify to resolve the pathology:** We must realize that without complete, unanimous cooperation and coordination, these problems will remain unresolved.

5. **Hold leaders accountable:** Leaders must report to us—all of us. They make the decisions, but we set the agenda. We all ultimately take responsibility for our fate.

6. **Implement the solutions:** We must resolve these problems which will require initial sacrifice, undoubtedly, for many individuals. But in the end, all of us will be far better off.

# Climate Change Our Biggest Problem?

The greatest fear is that climate change will continue *even without* our continued emissions of greenhouse gases. Most climate scientists have determined that a rise of another 1–1.5°C above current atmospheric temperatures could make a self-perpetuating rise (that is, temperatures continue rising without human-induced activity) of atmospheric temperatures possible. According to some models, this could occur as soon as 2040.

Although climate change, as stated above, appears to be our greatest problem, it is not. It is merely a symptom of a larger problem: the sociological dysfunction that exists in our world today. Our Supercivilization now has a fever as a result of a major illness. Why are we not addressing the following?

- The first decade of the 21st century saw growth rates in atmospheric $CO_2$ climb an average of 1.95 ppm/yr.

- According to NASA, the first decade of the 21st century was the hottest on record for the contiguous United States.

- Two years ago (2012) was the hottest year on record (shattering the previous record in 1998 by 0.6°C).

- Today $CO_2$ is 40 percent higher (395 ppm) than the average peak (285 ppm) of the last 2.1 million years.

- Fifteen million years ago was the last time we saw sustained $CO_2$ levels this high.

- $CO_2$ emissions increased 5.9 percent from 2009 to 2010 (highest absolute increase since the Industrial Revolution began).

- Atmospheric $CO_2$ levels this high in the past corresponded to a 2°C temperature increase above baseline. We will probably see a rise of another 1.4°C in the near future (years to a few decades) regardless of the changes we make in our $CO_2$ output.

## Summary: How Do We Resolve Humanity's Greatest Challenges of the 21st Century?

➤ We must first acknowledge the existence of The Super-civilization. Because of our biosociophysical reality today, we are a Supercivilization—one primary culture with one essential set of social norms and values. We have yet to acknowledge this.

➤ We must acknowledge our major problems. First and foremost is climate change. The Supercivilization is now diagnosed with a deadly illness (climate change), and we are still in the denial stage.

➤ Physical and biological problems are much easier to resolve than social problems. This makes the 21st century human extremely vulnerable to human-induced catastrophe.

➤ Our real solution to climate change and other "ill-nesses" resides squarely in our abilities to cooperate, communicate, and exchange ideas most beneficial to humankind as a whole. The social scientists of the 21st century will primarily be humankind's surgeons; they will be the ones to desperately operate on the ailing Supercivilization.

➤ The Mission Statement for Humanity is a tool we should use to reduce dangerous unpredictability in our world and to allow all of us to live at higher densities by creating more conformity without stifling individual freedom and creativity. We can then more effectively problem-solve.

# I. Biosociophysical Eras of Humanity

"If it walks like a duck, quacks like a duck, swims like a duck, feels like a duck, looks like a duck, and smells like a duck, it is probably a duck."

—Every doctor on this planet

# HOMININ HISTORY

## (or the History of Humans)

A brief overview of our heritage with regard to brain size

1600cc

1500cc

1400cc

1300cc

1200cc

1100cc

1000cc

900cc

800cc

700cc

600cc

500cc

400cc

*Australopithecus*
(*afarensis* and *africanus*
existed from 4 million to
2.5 million years ago.

*Ardipithecus species*
(*ramidus* and *kadabba*)
existed from 5.6 million
to 4.4 million years ago.

Brain Size

First nonspecific hominins
(all humans and their immediate
ancestors) first existed between
5 and 7 million years ago.

5 Million
Years Ago

*Homo neanderthalensis*
existed from 350,000 to
30,000 years ago.

*Homo sapiens* first existed
from 500,000 to 200,000
years ago.

*Homo heidelbergensis*
existed from 600,000
to 250,000 years ago.

*Homo erectus* existed
from 1.7 million to
140,000 years ago.

*Homo habilis* existed
from 2.3 to 1.4 million
years ago.

*Homo sapiens sapiens*
evolved out of Africa
approximately from
200,000 years ago and
are the anatomically
modern (not to
be confused with
sociologically modern)
humans.

**Present AD
2014**

# Chapter 1

# First Era of Humanity: Totally Nature Dependent
## (PRE–10,000 BC)

"God said … be fruitful and multiply and fill the earth and subdue it, and have dominion over … every living thing that moves on the earth."

—*Gen. 1:28 (King James Version)*

"In practice, we don't automatically have dominion; we have to fight for it. Nature has to be tamed. And this adversarial relationship with nature has governed our attitude toward it right up to the present day, hardening our sense of entitlement in the process."

—*Ian Tattersall, noted anthropologist, critically commenting on the above quotation from the Bible and humanity's view of nature*

# Brain Changes and Why They Occurred

Modern humans are unique in that no other organism (as far as we know) in our universe can think abstractly and imaginatively, reason, and contemplate their existence. Complex beings arose because of the predictability of the environment based upon laws of nature that could be understood by a rational being. As long as the environment (its biosociophysical characteristics) remains predictable, a complex, rational being will prevail. If the environment becomes too unpredictable (too dynamic) or too predictable (too static), it will favor simple organisms. A Goldilocks environment of dynamic predictability must occur that favors complex organisms. Because of the Goldilocks environment that existed over the last 4 million years on Earth, these specific characteristics have arisen in the hominin:

- Over the last 4 million years, our brain size increased from 400 to over 1300 cc.

- Most of our brain development occurred in the last 2 million years.

- Our neocortex (our rational, cognitive portion of higher brain function) had the greatest development; the limbic region (center of emotion) remained relatively unchanged.

- Anticipation and prognostication became adaptive advantages, leading to selection of a rational being.

- The limbic region remained as a result of the need for emotion to protect ourselves, protect our young, and procreate.

- Hominins thrived in an environment that obeyed the laws of nature (physics, chemistry, and mathematics), was rational, and hence was predictable.

# Before 10,000 BC Interconnectedness Was Extraordinarily Low

Before 10,000 BC, we had little interconnectedness. We had no realization of our place in the universe both geographically and temporally. We had little reason or capability to interact with others we didn't know existed. We had little capability to transport ourselves or communicate with others. This made our perceptions of our reality simple: our primary battle for survival was against nature. We had little understanding of nature and invented reasons for our existence: gods or godlike things determined us and our fate. If we understood why something occurred, we could use that understanding to help us survive.

The least of our problems were other people around us because it was the coordination and cooperation (especially the sharing of information) that allowed us to gain an advantage compared to other species. Because knowledge wasn't written or archived, other human beings around us were of extraordinary value, as they could teach us how to survive. We could also use a team approach (such as remaining in bands of 100–150 people) to fend off the natural world that was so potentially cruel to us.

## Why Are the Three Biosociophysical Eras So Important to Understand?

Humanity flourished at a critical period in the universe's existence. The rise of a complex being took place during a period of predictable dynamism in the universe. This development of understanding revealed repetitive patterns based upon mathematical and physical laws of the universe. When this pattern was slow and predictable enough (roughly 8 to 13.8 billion years after the universe was created) for a complex being to understand, that being would flourish. Prior to this period, the energy density was too great for a complex being to form. A complex being is probably predestined to traverse three biosociophysical periods (Figure 1.1) of existence anywhere in the universe.

- **Before the First Biosociophysical Era (before complex beings):** The inanimate was favored. The dynamism and energy density was so great that complex molecules couldn't form in the first 4 billion years. Between the 4 billion and 8 billion years after the Big Bang, complex molecules could form. There was still too much dynamism

**Hominins**

Humans and any of its preceding ancestors just after the split with chimpanzees.

**The Inanimate**

The remaining physical environment of the universe exclusive of the animate environment. (See Animate's definition on page 52)

The Supercivilization: Essential Concepts

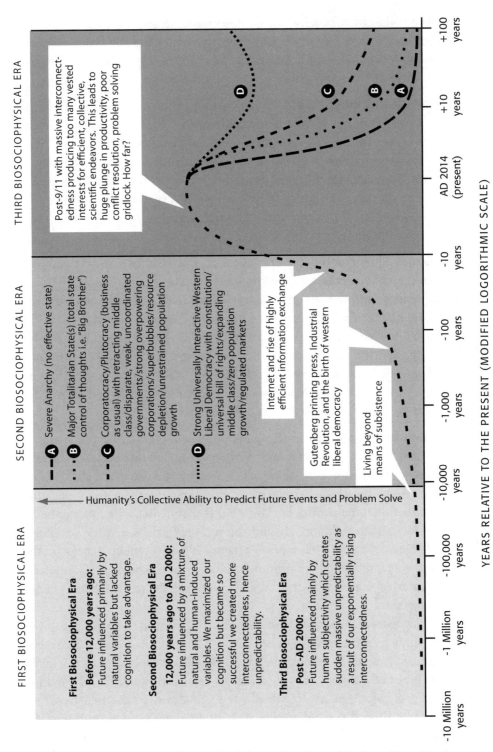

**FIGURE 1.1** The Essence of Science's Ability to Predict and Perhaps Even Manipulate the Future for the Benefit of Humanity

*This figure shows the relative predictability of our future in relation to our social structure and scientific capabilities.*

to favor the complex being, but complex molecules were forming in greater abundance. Between 8 and 12 billion years after the Big Bang, complex molecules could form life as a result of the decreasing energy densities and the increasing numbers of virgin complex molecular environments.

- **First Biosociophysical Era:** This occurs when the rise of a complex being is favored because of the predictability of the surrounding environment that allows an adaptive advantage for a complex, reasoning being. Interconnectedness is low and resources are abundant, which favors the growth of intelligence in these beings, as the environment is based on natural laws that can be taken advantage of by intelligence. Prior to this era, intelligent beings couldn't thrive, as there was too much energy-induced dynamism to favor the complex being.

- **Second Biosociophysical Era:** This occurs when the rise of a complex being attains a maximal growth stage because of increasing interconnectedness and the sharing of ideas which makes for a huge utilization of resources. The individuals—now social beings—who can share the most knowledge, not create it from scratch, are the most highly adaptable beings and the clear winners. This era can be officially ushered in only when individuals live beyond their means of subsistence, as the ability to acquire self-sustaining (and even self-ingratiating) goods and knowledge from others is the key to the rise of the social being.

- **Third Biosociophysical Era:** Population growth produces so much unpredictability that the rise of a complex being is no longer necessarily advantageous. The sociological being exists, and it is the rise of institutions that helps assist these beings into organizing their thoughts and navigating a more functional world. Socialization is mandatory. The rational being cannot exist in isolation. He and she can only exist when the sociological being most effectively manages the social environment. Because of the unpredictability of our environment and the control by powerful interests of knowledge needed by the rational individual, the rational being cannot solely exist.

It appears that complex beings throughout the universe are incapable of engaging in this hyperdynamism for very long. If so, we would have seen or heard from these complex beings by now. It appears we will never avoid the inevitable die-off, but we can try to delay it through the overarching and meticulous management of our institutions. Intellectual freedoms and blind social control are flip sides of a dangerous coin in this era; it is perhaps the reason why complex beings ultimately have a catastrophic fate throughout the universe. In our attempted resilience, an even balance must be achieved so we can maximize our chances of survival.

# Objective Measures of Interconnectedness and Resources

While not perfect, the formulas described below are attempts to put our inter-connectedness and resource use into perspective as it relates to the past, present, and future. By utilizing these formulas (Figure 1.2), they will help us see how truly unique our situation is and how our current culture of resource use is so hard to change. The lightning-quick drop in resources along with exponential growth in population are similar to the problems of a star at the end of its lifetime, particularly a supernova explosion: the bigger they are, the harder and more quickly they fall.

---

**Interconnectedness Communication Quotient (ICQ) of a Civilization**

$$ICQ = \frac{\text{Total population of the civilization}}{\text{(Total land area) x (Theoretical time to communicate between the two most distant individuals in that civilization)}}$$

---

**Interconnectedness Transportation Quotient (ITQ) of a Civilization**

$$ITQ = \frac{\text{Total population of the civilization}}{\text{(Total land area) x (Theoretical time to travel between the two most distant individuals in that civilization)}}$$

---

**Survivability Index of a Civilization in Relation to its Resource Base (SI)**

$$SI = ICQ \times \text{Resource availability}$$

---

### Unit Definitions

**Individuals living in a civilization:** people

**Total land area:** cubic kilometers (assuming one kilometer vertically in space by convention on the Earth for the third dimension)

**Theoretical time to travel/communicate between the two most distant individuals in the civilization:** seconds

**ICQ:** people/(km$^3$-seconds)

**ITQ:** people/(km$^3$-seconds)

**Resource availability:** known resources needed to support the contemporary standard of living for the entire population at that given period of time for a specified number of years into the future (measured in years)

**SI:** (people-years)/(km$^3$-seconds)

**FIGURE 1.2** Summary of Formulas (ICQ, ITQ, SI) Reflecting Our Interconnectedness

# The Major Concerns in Each Biosociophysical Era

Each biosociophysical era has challenges and concerns as a result of the specific characteristics of its time period; the ICQ/ITQ during each era reflects those characteristics. The concerns of each of the three eras are as follows:

- **First Biosociophysical Era:** Low interconnectedness (ICQ/ITQ) and a large amount of resources available (RA) equals a high resource Survivability Index (SI): In this era (Figure 1.3), we are in the greatest danger of nature-induced annihilation. This means relatively infrequent but huge die-offs. Growth is quite slow as our natural environment is so challenging that individual deaths occur often and at a young age because of the lack of understanding of our natural environment. We are spread so thinly, though, that local challenges doom mainly the individual and not humankind.

- **Second Biosociophysical Era:** Moderate interconnectedness (ICQ/ITQ) and a large amount of resources available (RA) equals a high resource Survivability Index (SI): The danger of a die-off stems roughly equally from ourselves and from nature. We begin to produce more of us thereby creating more social ills, but resources are still abundant. This is the exponential growth stage of humanity whereby nature is less problematic, but we ourselves and our problems become more so.

- **Third Biosociophysical Era:** High interconnectedness (ICQ/ITQ) and a declining resource base (RA) equals a sudden massive drop in the resource

| Time Period | ICQ [people/ (km³–seconds)] | ITQ [people/ (km³–seconds)] | SI [(people–years)/ (km³–seconds)] |
|---|---|---|---|
| 4,000,000 years ago | $2.33 \times 10^{-9}$ | $2.33 \times 10^{-9}$ | >1,000,000 |
| 1,000,000 years ago | $6.21 \times 10^{-10}$ | $6.21 \times 10^{-10}$ | >1,000,000 |
| 100,000 years ago | $1.55 \times 10^{-9}$ | $1.55 \times 10^{-9}$ | >1,000,000 |
| 12,000 years ago | $3.11 \times 10^{-10}$ | $3.11 \times 10^{-10}$ | >1,000,000 |
| At Birth of Christ | $1.24 \times 10^{-7}$ | $1.24 \times 10^{-7}$ | >1,000,000 |
| 1000 AD | $3.85 \times 10^{-7}$ | $3.85 \times 10^{-7}$ | >1,000,000 |
| 1900 AD | 0.179 | $5.97 \times 10^{-6}$ | 21.5 |
| 1950 AD | 5.59 | $2.33 \times 10^{-4}$ | 391 |
| 2000 AD | 13.4 | $5.59 \times 10^{-3}$ | 268 |

**FIGURE 1.3** Summary of ICQ, ITQ, and Resource Survivability Index (SI) for Human History (See Appendix for detailed calculations)

Survivability Index (SI): Complex organisms themselves are their greatest danger. Our cultural values that made us so successful in the first place cannot change quickly enough to match our exponential and lightning-fast drop in resources. This is a problem that apparently afflicts every complex organism throughout the universe as its exponential growth phase must be followed by catastrophe because of rising malevolence.

## General Description of the Human Being in the First Biosociophysical Era

- A rational being arises who can predict and anticipate the most basic aspects of the future. This era is sufficiently dynamic—but not too dynamic—to favor a rational being who can adapt to such an environment. It is a Goldilocks environment that is based on the laws of nature, is repetitively dynamic, and is predictable.

- This individual is still an emotive being. In order to procreate and protect one's own survival to promote one's genes, one must have as a core value that of living and promoting more individuals in that species. Without this irrational feature, life is impossible. Life is defined in part as an organism that has an internally homeostatic existence that protects this environment from failure.

- The external environment to the human being is still filled with more unknowns than knowns and therefore this adaptive advantage is only slight in creating only a small, but steady, advantage for the rational being and its offspring.

- Massive die-offs are rare but near total. Smaller, localized die-offs are the rule given our low interconnectedness. These die offs are mainly from natural factors and occur more in the young to middle age. Few people live beyond a decade or two.

# Egalitarian Nature of Humanity Pre-10,000 BC

Most anthropologists surmise that the hunter-gatherer prior to 10,000 BC had, for the most part, an egalitarian existence. This meant that individuals worked cooperatively and without hierarchy to survive. Characteristics of this environment are as follows:

- **Low interconnectedness:** The major problems of the environment were not fully understood, and therefore humans had far more options to interact with others. Socialization wasn't mandatory. Bands of individuals could split from one another as no one was directly dependent on another for survival. The division of labor had not occurred beyond the family and direct care for the young. Knowledge was shared to only a limited extent.

- **Lack of sedentism:** This meant that individuals were not burdened by the need to remain in the same location; people could and would move about and not remain as slaves to their current physical environment.

- ***Voluntary* nature of interaction:** Individuals wanted to band together because all individuals needed each other's help in the face of unknown unknowns that even the most knowledgeable individuals didn't fully understand. Disagreements, while present, were inconsequential given the natural factors that could destroy the entire group swiftly and effectively.

# Advantages of Sharing Information (Rise of the Social Being) and the End of Human Versus Nature

As interconnectedness slowly increases and populations rise (Figure 1.4), social interactions become a greater determinant of adaptive success. The social being becomes the greatest, most adaptive being. The most rational rarely wins. Why?

- The rational being who is isolated is of limited value because knowledge and not logic are the key drivers of success.

- Controlling information is far more advantageous than creating information from scratch.

- Those who control information, control others. This includes controlling the most rational, intelligent beings too. The rational being must decide what to study and needs resources to do so. The social being wins the war of attrition because he or she controls these two factors.

- When socialization is mandatory, egalitarian relationships decline; those in control of the means of production can manipulate those not in control.

| | FIRST: HUMAN vs NATURE (BEFORE 10,000 BC) | SECOND: HUMAN vs NATURE AND HUMAN (BETWEEN 10,000 BC and 2000 AD) | THIRD: HUMAN vs HUMAN (AFTER 2000 AD) |
|---|---|---|---|
| Density (People/Total Surface Land Area of Earth in Sq Km) | <0.006 | Between 0.006 and 40 | >40 |
| ICQ at Beginning of Era | $2.33 \times 10^{-9}$ | $3.11 \times 10^{-10}$ | 13.4 |
| ITQ at Beginning of Era | $2.33 \times 10^{-9}$ | $3.11 \times 10^{-10}$ | $5.59 \times 10^{-3}$ |
| Resource Survivability Index at Beginning of Era | Near infinite | Near infinite | 268 |
| Predominant Social Structure | Hunter-gatherer | Tribes to ultimate nation-states | Supercivilization |
| Predominant Micro-Interpersonal Relations | Family | Family | Family |
| Predominant Macro-Interpersonal Relations | Egalitarian | Mixed egalitarian and hierarchical | Hierarchical |
| Individual Empowerment Over Others | Limited | Significant | Potentially massive |
| Involvement With Others | Voluntary (mutually beneficial) | Compelling but potentially constricting | Mandatory |
| Knowledge | Limited | Ideal | Too much |
| Intelligence | High | Higher | Highly |
| Predictability of Surrounding Environment (Conducive to Good Science) | Predictable | Less predictable | Unpredictable |
| Potential Success in Problem Solving (Conducting the Best Science) | Limited | Significant | Massive unpredictability and inappropriate applications |
| Actual Success in Problem Solving (Conducting the Best Science) | Modest | Significant | Problematic because of unpredictability and inappropriate applications |
| Humanity's Primary Challenge for Survival | Nature | Other humans and nature | Other humans |

FIGURE 1.4   Comparison of the Three Biosociophysical Eras of Humanity

# Second Era of Humanity: Human and Nature Dependent, Pre-modern Period
## (10,000 BC–AD 1900)

"Civilizations are fragile, impermanent things. …
Civilizations are fleeting things."

—*Joseph A. Tainter, author of The Collapse of Complex Societies*

# Rationality-Irrationality Paradox

As we use logical conclusions to overcome major hurdles of survivability in our world, we create a less rational world around ourselves. There are simply more of us (greater interconnectedness) creating more problem-solving challenges of human origin. Thus the rational world becomes markedly less rational, and we become less capable of anticipating future events. Hence, we see the rise of the Second Biosociophysical Era of Humanity and the pre-modern social being.

## The Rise of Irrationality

Seven key factors have led to a less rational existence. These factors have forced us to cooperate with each other, and the end result is a world requiring social interaction. To achieve success, one must interact on an irrational level. The seven key factors are as follows:

- **Living beyond our means of subsistence:** Goods must be traded; the division of labor demands specialization and hence cooperation.

- **Population density increase:** Navigating the social world requires interacting with others who are unpredictable. With such close quarters, individuals must coordinate their movements.

- **Resources become finite:** Resources are not endless. Attaining those resources requires cooperation, and those who claim those resources as their own must cooperate with those who do not. No one benefits without bartering.

- **Increased life span:** Longer life spans allow more information to flow between generations, which creates more accumulated information over generations. The dependence upon those who hold the information becomes critical, and hence a glue between distant humans (both geographically and temporally) begins to take hold.

- **New technological developments:** This requires a division of labor to run machines no matter how primitive the machines are. Information must be exchanged to further develop the technology.

- **Increased resource demand:** As we develop new technology, we create greater demands on our resource base. These demands require new ways of refining and transporting the resources, thus requiring cooperation.

- **Increased waste products:** Emissions affect others around us from all six factors above, and the need to deal with these requires cooperation.

# Universal Cooperation: Is It Even Possible?

Many believe that universal cooperation is either impossible or dangerous. However, what most people don't realize is that universal cooperation has occurred with great success in the past and will continue to be a critical means of dealing with human-induced problems. Universal cooperation is such a difficult challenge for three reasons:

- **Behavioral entropy:** We, as a Supercivilization, cannot decide what the perfect nonrandom state is. In physics those laws are determined by formulas. In biology, there is no law; it is completely discretionary.

- **Discretionary energy:** All individuals are trying to accomplish an end, and to get to that end, we are expending large amounts of energy. However, no one can definitively coordinate that energy.

- **Individual freedom versus societal rights:** The more interconnected we become, the more likely contradictions grow between individual and societal rights. For the first time, we are all in one crowded theatre (not multiple theatres—one), and the cackling of even one individual can ruin the viewing experience of every person, potentially causing a riot. Never before has this happened in our history as humans.

  Our lives depend on complete uniformity on many important issues (such as climate change, vaccinations, terrorism). We have already achieved enormous success with universal cooperation on some issues. Smallpox eradication is the most obvious example. We must harness universal cooperation to resolve the tremendous variety of issues we will face as a Supercivilization.

# Moser Biological Uncertainty Principle

I propose the Moser biological uncertainty principle to explain why humanity has tremendous difficulty with problem-solving in the 21st century. It is described as follows:

- Because future events can never be predicted (Quantum Mechanics leading to the Heisenberg Uncertainty Principle on a very small scale), no one can predict the future with utmost certainty. Never. In the inanimate world, laws can estimate the mathematical chances of something happening in the future with great reliability on a large scale. When trying to study and predict the behavior of a complex being, this scientific study currently becomes problematic.

- Because we understand the concept of behavioral feedback as a species, our future is particularly unstable and unpredictable. In an environment full of complex biological organisms who can reason, these predictions become less effective because of instantaneous feedback to and from our subjects of study. We call this reflexivity.

- Thomas Kuhn argues that an objective scientist cannot be divorced from his/her subject. We always have discretionary powers to study our subject matter—whatever we want to study and however we want to study it. We don't notice this effect when we study the natural (inanimate) world, because our predictions have little influence on our subject matter. If our subject matter is a complex biological organism, we hopelessly try to study this organism without great success.

- Because of this power to choose what we study and affect what we study, we cannot predict our results (or the future). As our studies focus more on us and our problems, our science breaks down.

- If we believe we can control the future (and particularly behavior), those who convince us they can control the future (and particularly our actions) will control our thoughts, minds, and imaginations through paradigms. In the past, arbiters between a God, or gods, traditionally promoted a religious paradigm and held that role as clergy. Scientists have become our undisputed clergy today because of this false premise regarding the sanctity of scientific discovery.

## Pre-modern period (pre-AD 1900)

During this period the implied consent of all humans is not necessary to perform basic tasks of daily living and maintaining personal sustenance for each individual. We still control our future without the necessary assistance by all of humanity.

## Behavioral entropy

Biological systems do not adhere to "mathematical laws" of nature. The greater the intelligence of a biological organism, the more likely the organism will understand "mathematical laws" and rise above those laws. Individuals who understand those laws will not respond to those laws predictably. This unpredictable response to "mathematical laws" is called behavioral entropy. The greater the intelligence of an organism, the less predictable the response. Science breaks down.

## Moser biological uncertainty principle

The more biologically dense the environment, the less certainty there is in our environment. Scientific success depends on predicting the future. Because of biology and our inherent ability to reflexively interact with our environment, we can never predict our future.

- When our science becomes refined, fine-tuned, and focused, particularly on our biology, it loses its edge. The more specific we make our conclusions about our behavior, the less effective it becomes. Science breaks down. Rational problem solving is no longer supremely effective.

## The Predominant Type of Being

I argue that humans and perhaps all complex beings traverse three stages of biosociophysical development. Each stage is predominated by a means of fundamental problem-solving. The type of being in each of the three stages is as follows:

- **Rational being:** Rational thought was the ultimate way that humans triumphed over their biosociophysical environment (First Biosociophysical Era).

- **Social being:** The individuals with the most information and those who control the information and control others by choosing when and to whom to present that information are the triumphant ones (Second Biosociophysical Era).

- **Sociological being:** The individuals who control the institutions that control the information flow that control others are the triumphant ones (Third Biosociophysical Era). Control is less transparent and therefore more effective. This allows for more subtle manipulation.

## Humanity's Rising Social Struggle

One simple and straightforward measure of the types of challenges humans faced in the past was to assess the cause of death of individuals during those periods (Figure 2.1A to C). Those dying from natural or inanimate causes were most likely facing challenges against nature; those who were dying from human-induced causes were most likely facing challenges between humans.

- As humans advance as social beings, more of the causes of death are because of social causes *under our control* and less because of natural causes out of our control.

- Death becomes more discretionary to the individual as we advance through human history. One controls one's time of death more so today than at any other time in our history as a species.

- As irrationality increases, the view of humans toward death, risk, and dangerous behaviors becomes controlled by powerful interests. Our behavior is no longer controlled by seemingly innate drives or mysterious unknowns of the environment.

- Humans become convinced by powerful interests that death and dying must be accepted as a reasonable alternative to the here and now. Being socially accepted is worth the calculated risks even if the behavior in question is totally irrational or even dangerous.

# Causes of Death in Paleolithic Humans (Pre-10,000 BC)

## Evidence in Our Gene Pool

The gene pool is quite homogeneous in humans (99.9 percent of DNA base pairs are the same in all humans), which suggests a recent single ancestor. This homogeneity in humans, in spite of our existence dating back to at least 5 million years, suggests die-offs were probably near total and numbered perhaps in the dozens (at a minimum). Current literature reflects the following:

- Near-total die-offs occurred relatively frequently with the most recent one as late as 74,000 years ago.

- Modern Adam and Eve existed approximately 200,000 years ago suggesting massive, comprehensive die-offs every few thousand to hundreds of thousands of years (Y-chromosome and mitochondrial DNA analysis).

- The *homininae* subfamily consists of only five species. Chimpanzees, one of the five species members, has a population of only 100,000–200,000 today, yet this species has more gene variability than all 7 billion humans. In comparison, Class Insectae has 900,000 species with 350,000 beetle species alone suggesting far fewer near universal die offs in their history.

- It appears the more complex the organism, the more likely that organism's population experiences a near-total die-off over a given period of time.

- As few as 18,500 hominins existed roughly 1.2 million years ago, also reflecting cyclical die-offs and not just one single die-off in the last 200,000 years.

## Evidence in Geological and Astronomical Records

Geological and astronomical records point to die-offs every 50,000 years or less. Supervolcanoes and asteroid impacts are the most likely and problematic of natural catastrophic events. Other types of unknown events might have occurred also, but we cannot say for sure. The literature reflects the following:

- According to the Smithsonian Institution, one major VEI-7 event has occurred every 1000 to 2000 years during the last 10,000 years from a supervolcano (with a significant human threat).

- A VEI-8 event, which could be biosphere-threatening, has occurred roughly every 50,000 years or so (26,000 years ago and 74,000 years ago are already verified).

- Asteroid collisions are even more frequent with major consequences similar to supervolcanoes. Asteroid impacts (asteroids greater than 1 km in diameter) make near-total human die-offs in the past even more frequent than every 50,000 years from supervolcanoes alone.

## VEI (Volcanic Explosivity Index)

A logarithmic scale created by geologists to classify volcanoes and their potential size of eruption. The scale is from 1 (small) to 8 (large).

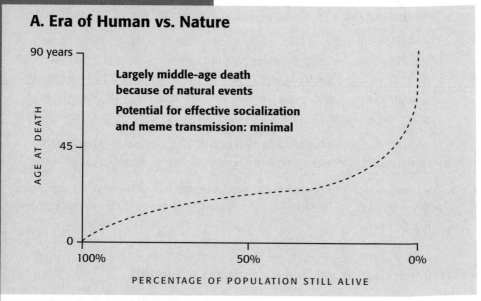

## A. Era of Human vs. Nature

Largely middle-age death because of natural events

Potential for effective socialization and meme transmission: minimal

AGE AT DEATH — 90 years, 45, 0

PERCENTAGE OF POPULATION STILL ALIVE — 100%, 50%, 0%

FIGURE 2.1 A  Biosociophysical Eras of Humanity: Life Span Curve of the Population—General Trends (Conceptual Only)

The Supercivilization: Essential Concepts

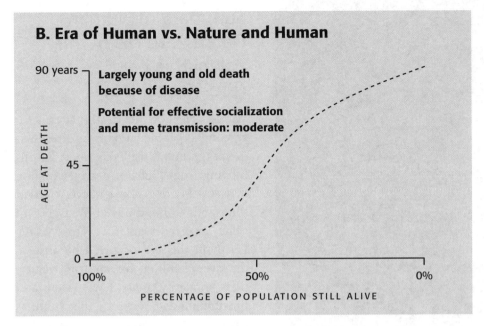

FIGURE 2.1 B   Biosociophysical Eras of Humanity: Life Span Curve of the Population—General Trends (Conceptual Only)

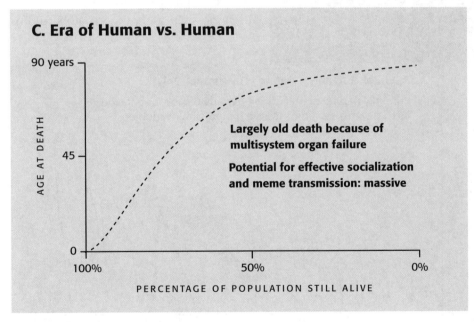

FIGURE 2.1 C   Biosociophysical Eras of Humanity: Life Span Curve of the Population—General Trends (Conceptual Only)

## Evapotranspiration

Combined evaporation from surface water and transpiration (evaporation from aerial portions of a plant's leaves). In general, the higher the latitude, the lower the rate.

## Summary of Human Death Patterns in the Paleolithic Era (Pre-10,000 BC)

We do not know the death patterns for sure in Paleolithic humans, as direct evidence is scant. Most likely, large die-offs ranging from highs of nearly a million to as few as a few thousand every tens of thousands to hundreds of thousands of years occurred regularly (Figure 2.2A). Death in this era occurred because of the overwhelming threats from nature that humanity must have faced and the unbounded territory that humans roamed in. Human populations probably had slow rises with smaller die-offs of more frequent variability affecting isolated groups caused by local challenges, such as large predators and/or

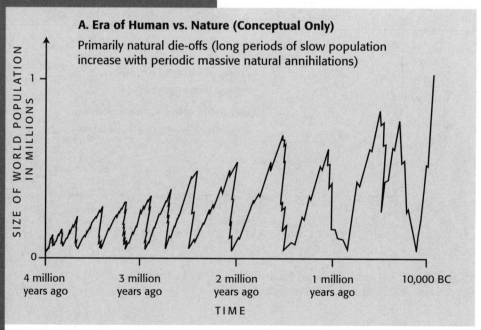

**A. Era of Human vs. Nature (Conceptual Only)**

Primarily natural die-offs (long periods of slow population increase with periodic massive natural annihilations)

FIGURE 2.2 A   Biosociophysical Eras of Humanity: Population Changes over Time—General Trends

The Supercivilization: Essential Concepts

climate changes. Humans had little understanding of the universe and little ability to interact with each other over long distances. Therefore, information sharing between individuals was highly limited, thereby making social problems extremely irrelevant on a large scale.

## Causes of Death in the Mesolithic Period (10,000–8,000 BC)

As a result of the presence of more archeological as well as fossil records, the Mesolithic Period is much more forthcoming in information than the Paleolithic Period. This period reveals several following issues that offer clues about how individuals died during this era (Figure 2.2B):

- This period is known for a warming world with warming fully completed by 8,000 BC. This allowed for more temperate latitudes for humans to reside in, creating more areas for evapotranspiration to decrease. This made domestication of plants and animals more conducive and water storage and transport easier.

- Humans became sedentary, because they could no longer hunt big game (humans had killed big game off a few thousand years earlier). They had to watch over their possessions, thus creating communities of roaming hunter-gatherers.

- Humans started producing goods and services and lived beyond their means of subsistence particularly in the Fertile Crescent of Asia, which was the cradle of early civilization. Because of its superior natural resources supporting farming, its climate, and its centralized proximity of human development, this was the perfect area for civilizations to take root.

- This period was marked by relatively little disease but increased violence because of the need to socialize and navigate in a world with a division of labor.

- Disease occurred infrequently because few comorbidities existed in humans (people died quickly), there was less transmissibility as a result of decreased densities, and domestication of animals (that could transmit zoonotic diseases) had not been fully realized.

- Violence increased because higher population densities along with more goods and services meant that people found it easier to steal than to obtain or produce goods through hard work. As natural problems became less dire and mysterious, disagreements became more common.

- Humans start to live slightly longer (average life span into the high 20s and early 30s) because of our success against natural problems such as large predators and sudden climate changes.

## Causes of Death in the Neolithic Period (8000 BC–4000 BC)

The Neolithic Period offers the first evidence of widespread farming and animal husbandry, which creates a greater surplus leading to more human activities outside the realm of basic subsistence support. This surplus leads to all of the following (Figure 2.2B):

- A nascent science of domestication of plants and animals develops, leading to more surpluses, as we study how to create techniques for creating more food.

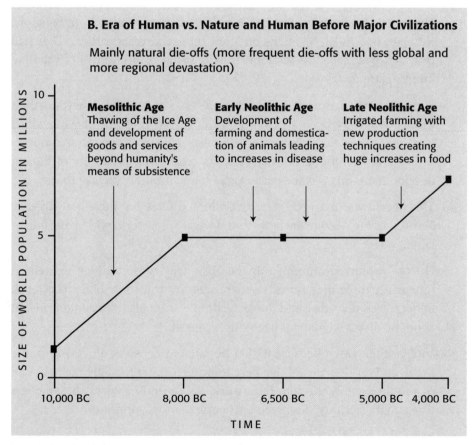

FIGURE 2.2 B   Biosociophysical Eras of Humanity: Population Changes over Time—General Trends

- The first bureaucracies arise to oversee the goods and services produced during this era. This allows for more efficient trade and accounting.

- Deaths from disease increase, as densities of humans increase, and zoonotic diseases increase as a result of people living in close quarters with domesticated animals.

- Life span and population growth starts to stabilize after previous growth periods. With more diseases present, the young start to die at a higher rate, while more people turn older beyond reproductive age because of the elimination of predators.

- Violent injuries from fighting seems to remain constant after the Mesolithic Period, but accidental injuries appear to decline. Thus, violence appears to comprise a higher proportion of earlier death and injuries than in previous times.

- More chronic illnesses and caring for the sick occurs, which helps foster more comorbidities and more disease during this period. For the first time, chronic disease, such as tuberculosis, appears in the archeological record.

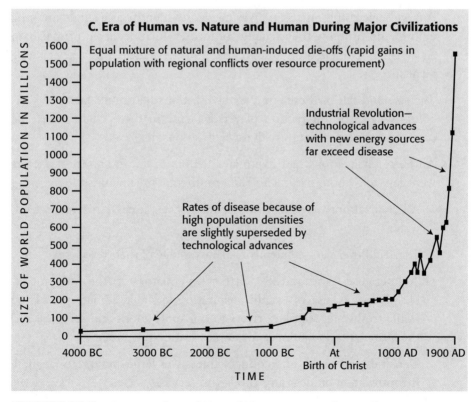

**FIGURES 2.2 C**    Biosociophysical Eras of Humanity: Population Changes over Time—General Trends

# Causes of Death During the Rise of Ancient Civilizations (4000 BC–AD 500)

Previously, the rise of metallurgy was viewed as a key factor in the development of the ancient civilizations. As more is learned, historians argue, however, other factors influence the growth of these civilizations. It becomes clear that the rise of these ancient civilizations meant they also fell at some point, as they no longer exist today. Did the same issues that caused the death of individuals also cause the death of these civilizations? Here is what most historians concede about the six major ancient civilizations on the Eurasian continent with regard to their rise and fall and deaths of its people (Figure 2.2C):

- The main advance allowing comprehensive civilizations to exist was large-scale irrigation and the use of water to develop large-scale farming. Massive success in creating food required an extensive bureaucracy with great planning, accounting, and leadership.

- Metals such as copper, bronze, and iron allowed more efficiency in obtaining goods and services. With the development of effective tools, thereby making resource surpluses possible, work was far less tedious.

- A large scale common culture was needed to identify as a single unifying culture and promote the exchange of ideas, which occurred primarily in Asia. The documentation and archiving of these ideas was a key to long term success.

- The rise and fall of these complex civilizations had multi-factorial variables. Synergistic interaction played a factor in these civilizations' life spans and the type of culture these civilizations displayed.

- All these civilizations had five major factors in common. These factors were caused by both natural and environmental precipitants:

  » All civilizations were near the world's best resources, particularly fresh water.

  » These cultures very efficiently took advantage of their resources.

  » Temperate areas around 35° North of the equator were the most amenable places because of evapotranspiration, a stable climate producing stable freshwater supplies, rivers to transport goods and services, and the best plants and animals for domestication purposes.

  » Densities and hence interconnectedness was large enough to facilitate the movement of ideas and goods and services.

  » These civilizations had room to expand without stretching the logistical supply chains too thin, thereby making a unifying culture possible.

Mountains and oceans were impassable, unlike valleys and rivers.

- None of these civilizations died out from a single natural catastrophic event; rather a multitude of social and natural factors determined their fate. It was the interaction between a complex list of social and natural factors that led to their downfall or their success.

- Similarly, the most prosperous civilizations had the highest densities. Its citizens tended to die from war, disease, and natural factors. Those humans who were not members of one of the major civilizations still battled and died mainly from the hands of nature. The rise of a warlike state fighting cultural and resource wars marked the era of the ancient civilizations. During this period, humanity's sole concern for survival was slowly being replaced by a concern for maintaining cultural and resource hegemony.

- Most of the time these civilizations were replaced by more efficient bureaucracies from other portions of the continents and did not die out from natural resource problems. It was social infighting that created their downfall as the downfall of one civilization led to another episode of a more efficient resource procurement system. If resources or natural factors were

## Six major complex civilizations

Mesopotamian, Egyptian, Roman, Greek, Chinese, and Indus Valley

the only precipitant to failure, one would not see the sprouting of newer civilizations over these same areas.

- The near-monopoly on death from natural causes was fast fading, as we were now battling for ideas and goods and services that would allow us to fight nature more effectively.

## Fall of the Roman Empire: Why?

The Roman Empire is a great case study, because so much is known about this civilization and its collapse. Many historians point to a variety of factors that led to the downfall. The general consensus of what happened is as follows:

- Rome lost procurement and logistical advantages it once had (water-centered supply line versus land) in accessing its resource base. Resources became harder to procure as the Roman Empire tried to conquer territories located in inland areas lacking natural supply lines (oceans, seas, or rivers) that could be easily and inexpensively accessed.

- A decrease in the ICQ/ITQ contributed to poor tactical and strategic decision making. Smaller groups like the Huns who had a smaller, more centralized leadership could make tactical and even strategic decisions more quickly and effectively.

- Rome lost the ability to maintain its cultural values in its occupying areas. Loss of cultural identity and homogeneity, which caused a loss of the social glue holding the empire together, made for easy insurrection.

## Generalized Lifecycle of a Civilization

There are several stages in the rise and fall of a civilization. Civilizations will typically rise and fall or at least merge with other civilizations. One continuous civilization has never before existed. The stages of a civilization include the following:

1. **Initial overwhelming growth:** Vast available resources with low interconnectedness makes for a high Survival Index (SI).

2. **Continued resource procurement:** Systems for procurement are refined and become highly successful, allowing for cheap production of goods and services.

3. **Geographical expansion:** With the surplus of goods and services comes the ability to expand to areas with additional resources and wealth.

4. **Difficulty in procurement and centralized communication and coordination:** Decisions need to be made as the ICQ/ITQ decrease because of

prolonged procurement lines. These decisions either are delayed, or local decisions, which may impact surrounding portions of the civilization, make for tremendous waste and cost implementation.

5. **Minor stressors cause catastrophic synergistic failures:** Minor stressors, such as war, disease, or famine occur, which seal a civilization's fate. These stressors result from low interconnectedness, which does not allow an identifying centralized culture to thrive. The lower interconnectedness (decreased ICQ/ITQ) brings poor coordination and even ambivalence about surrounding areas of the civilization. However, because interconnectedness is low, the civilization dies a slow death. In its death, instead of self-annihilation, it splinters and fragments into smaller less productive civilizations.

## Tale of Two Civilizations (Eastern and Western Roman Empires)

Perhaps no failed civilization has garnered more attention than the fall of the Roman Empire. It is subject to much historical debate and few would argue that its fate was tied to the decision making of its leaders. The big question is: When the Empire was split into two portions, why did one side succeed (The Eastern portion) and the other side regress into the Middle Ages? Here is a comparison of the two portions:

- Eastern portion (Byzantine Empire): This included a water-centered strategy with easier logistics for better procurement of resources, more centralized control by a government, and a single unifying culture. Over time this was a civilization that thrived for over one thousand years.

- Western portion (Holy Roman Empire): This was a land-based civilization with more difficult procurement issues and weakened governance; the rise of the Middle Ages saw little economic, political, or technological growth. Five important factors led to these dismal results:

  » The retardation of intellectual stimulation and idea sharing as a result of the weakness of a centralized system of government with low interconnectedness.

  » A centralized dogma of one world view promoted by the Catholic church that stubbornly tried, with little ability, to transmit its power to control individuals who were separated by geographical hurdles (mountains). Fear was the main conduit for control rather than positive reinforcement to encourage creativity. The Church discouraged anyone from challenging its sacred dogma that remained frozen in time for hundreds of years.

» Weakened governments with decentralized and anemic bureaucracies resulted because the Church wanted to control every facet of governance. Confusion lay in the minds of many as to who was the real leader: the Pope or the King.

» A dramatic increase in population densities to unprecedented levels because of resource bases that were for that moment adequate. Interconnectedness grows making insurrection considerably more likely, should the standard of living worsen.

» Unparalleled development of human disease forced a profoundly different world view. Individuals soon surmise that conditions can indeed become worse by doing nothing and that being creative can help one's situation in spite of the teachings of the Catholic church.

## Sawtooth Patterns and Models of Population Growth

During this period, the population growth of humans is at its greatest sustained rate. Most population growth throughout human history occurs through cyclical changes. Rarely is the population static or linear in its changes. A die-off (the back of a sawtooth; see Figure 2.2C) occurs because conditions change that no longer favor the prolonged growth of that species population. Some cycles are so slow and long that they are unnoticed and there is an illusion of smooth linear growth. Some are so quick and small that they are hardly noticeable. The goal we all hope for is reducing these cycles to being inconsequential.

Typically, an insult occurs to a population and then the population with a high ICQ/ITQ discovers how to combat that problem and then the population increases until the next insult. The greater the dynamics (that is, the higher the ICQ/ITQ), the more dynamic these sawtooth patterns turn out to be (more frequent, smaller sawtooths). Natural causes of die-offs tend to be hypodynamic, last longer, and are more predictable. Human causes of die-offs tend to be hyperdynamic, quite short, and unpredictable.

## How to Avoid Sawtooth Patterns of Population Growth

Avoiding these population insults should be at the forefront of our minds given our highly interconnected world today. A few things we should remember:

- Die-offs are almost unavoidable in high ICQ/ITQ environments.

- Biological systems with feedback (both virtuous and vicious cycles) are fundamental to biological systems. These systems of feedback are both self-defeating and self-correcting. When a population substantially increases its interconnectedness, self-induced die-offs inevitably become a reality.

- Feedback cycles still occur in lower ICQ/ITQ environments but are much less dynamic.

- The sawtooth patterns are more frequent and less severe in environments that share information quickly—problems arise quicker, expand quicker, but are extinguished more quickly.

- Unquestionably, during the expansion phase of a population of a complex organism (Figure 2.2C and D) in which ITQ and ICQ are of moderating quantity, die-offs become of little notice or even inconsequential to the population at large. Our goal is to moderate our ICQ/ITQ to allow continued efficient growth in our standard of living and eliminate the possibility of a die-off.

- We are left with three important ways to counteract these cycles (reduce our ICQ/ITQ, increase our resource availability or RA):

  » We must voluntarily decrease our population growth or even decrease our total population to reduce the ICQ/ITQ.

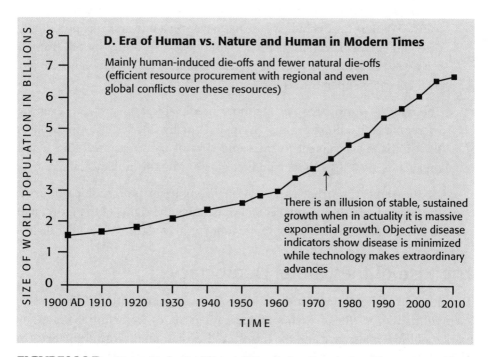

FIGURES 2.2 D   Biosociophysical Eras of Humanity: Population Changes over Time —Recent Population Growth and Projected Trends

» We must create additional resources to sustain densities with better technology to continue improving our standard of living (increase resource availability or increase RA).

» We must find new habitats in which to expand the population to decrease the ICQ/ITQ.

## The Renaissance to the Industrial Revolution (AD 1500–1900)

The Renaissance is known in western civilization as a time in which a flurry of new creativity and massive social change takes place to improve our understanding of our world. Five key factors about this period make it particularly significant:

- Realization that the world is finite. The world doesn't go on forever and resources are not unlimited. The voyage of Christopher Columbus is symbolic and emblematic of this realization.

- The world begins to make sense on a scientific level (laws of the inanimate are created, such as the laws of thermodynamics or Newton's laws of motion). All events are ultimately explained by natural forces. All events have a logical cause based upon the laws of mathematics, physics, and chemistry. We become less anthropocentric in believing the universe was "ours." We start to conclude we are bit players in a universe that potentially has mathematical certainty. We are no longer a separate, special feature, but a fully integrated part of our universe, subject to "its" laws and not our own beliefs or superstitions.

- The natural world becomes far more predictable now and can even be overcome with a more rational mind. Eventually Charles Darwin explains that humans are subject to the same laws of nature as are other living organisms, creating rationalism that crosses into the biological realm.

- At the same time that these rational, empirical philosophies flourish (because of new-found intellectual freedoms), the rights of the individual to think independently becomes far more protected (the rise of liberalism).

## The Rise of the Liberal Democracy

The rise of the liberal democracy (a democratic country with full liberties as exemplified by the Bill of Rights in the United States Constitution) is a key marker of the Renaissance and the Industrial Revolution. It is the ultimate form of rational governance, and to some, like Francis Fukuyama, it is the last form of government. Liberal democracy is a tremendous advance, and its rise is described as follows:

- The world goes from zero democracies before the Renaissance to 40 in 1972 to 120 in 2000.

- Liberal democracies go from zero in 1900 to 89 in 2009, comprising 46 percent of the world's population.

- The liberal democracy has the potential to allow the greatest number of ideas the best opportunity to flourish. As a formalized institution that allows creativity to succeed, a liberal democracy filters out the least productive ideas that offer the least utility for the entire population.

- The liberal democracy is potentially the fairest way to advance the needs of every person of society. This gives legitimacy to an idea without having to worry about overt coercive measures from "others."

- The upside is that a liberal democracy can rapidly change to match a dynamic environment created by such high ICQ/ITQ environments through an overarching paradigm (or what I call a prion) instillation.

- The downside is that prognosticating events in the future becomes hugely problematic. It helps control the behavioral entropy through mandatory socialization, but if that entropy is unleashed (that is, if the liberal democracy

## Prion (as social metaphor)

From the words protein and infection. These are ideas—expressed as social metaphors—shared by more than one person. They possess the potential to control all of us and force us to think only in paradigmatic terms. For more information, see Chapter 9.

## Discretionary problem solving

This is the ability of humans to determine which problems exist and how to solve them. In the First Biosociophysical Era, the problems were local, natural, and mainly beyond our comprehension. In the Second Biosociophysical Era, discretionary problem solving became more pronounced. By the beginning of the Third Biosociophysical Era of Humanity, our mandatory existence as primarily a complex, social being (the sociological being) has created a socialized version of humans in which discretionary problem solving is no longer advantageous but is highly problematic.

## Pre-modern sociological human

Humans (pre-AD 1900) have options to become social beings. In order to exist, we do not rely on implied consent by all humans. We can choose to be manipulated or controlled by society at large.

fails or even portions fail), then catastrophic self-annihilation is a major threat. Synergistic catastrophe through a domino effect of events becomes possible, even probable, in a hyperdynamic world.

## The Potential for Catastrophe with the Liberal Democracy

While liberal democracy may be the final form of government, it has major problems from a purely sociological perspective. It further creates behavioral entropy and thus makes our unpredictability highly problematic. It allows us all to function at higher levels of interconnectedness with organized creativity, but if it becomes a failure, it leaves all of us with catastrophic interconnectedness (higher densities consuming vast resources that we were never capable of using without a liberal democracy firmly in place). Problem-solving will become impossible if the liberal democracy is usurped. Synergistic self-annihilation becomes a reality if the right type of government is not in place. The major problems are summarized as follows (Figure 2.2E):

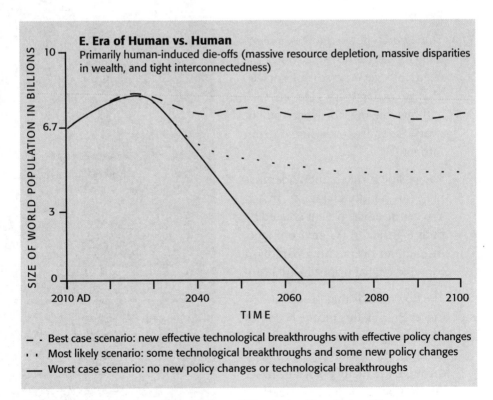

**E. Era of Human vs. Human**
Primarily human-induced die-offs (massive resource depletion, massive disparities in wealth, and tight interconnectedness)

SIZE OF WORLD POPULATION IN BILLIONS

TIME

— · Best case scenario: new effective technological breakthroughs with effective policy changes
· · Most likely scenario: some technological breakthroughs and some new policy changes
— Worst case scenario: no new policy changes or technological breakthroughs

**FIGURES 2.2 E** Biosociophysical Eras of Humanity: Population Changes over Time—Recent Population Growth and Projected Trends

The Supercivilization: Essential Concepts

- With so much freedom to speak and create new ideas, a greater potential exists for the manipulation of the minds of others; persuasion becomes too effective.

- Instead of one paradigm, as what occurred in the Middle Ages, several paradigms now compete for our attention as a result of our increased freedoms and interconnectedness.

- We are bound to change our minds on a multitude of subjects based upon faulty arguments proposed by the loudest voices (vesting of interests to ideas). Change is good, but only when change is congruent with reality; that rarely occurs, except in a stable (carefully coordinated and cooperative) liberal democracy. Ideas need to percolate in, not merely indoctrinate members of, society.

- With the rise of technology and economic prosperity comes more discretionary problem-solving—the essence of the sociologically modern human. The pre-modern sociological human vanishes.

## Overall View of Death at the End of the 1800s

Death is no longer a complete mystery. We are still dying at extremely high rates, but we can now study death and see if we can extend life with a rationalism that has been successfully applied to the physical sciences. The facts about this period are as follows:

- Our life expectancy is at or just slightly above the life expectancy of individuals at the time of the Mesolithic Period.

- Death is viewed as causative and not punitive or happenstance; nature can be tamed and perhaps even controlled. However, we do not have the means to combat nature, and therefore deaths are still mainly a natural occurrence of unknown etiology.

- Humanity's numbers skyrocket as resource surpluses from the Industrial Revolution triple the population (from 500 million to 1.6 billion in 400 years) increasing densities and thereby making communicable diseases highly problematic.

- We develop a view that we can figure our way out of nearly any problem using logic and rational thought in a cooperative fashion. The scientific method is overtaking our culture and hence the biological sciences.

# Chapter 3

# Second Era of Humanity: Human and Nature Dependent, Modern Period

## (AD 1900–AD 2000)

"Being rich now means having enough money that you don't have to encounter anyone who isn't."

—*Robert Reich, former US secretary of labor*

# Logic: Our Savior?

At the beginning of the 20th century logic becomes a profoundly important part of human advancement. It has created so many advantages for humans that we now see it as the future of human growth and success. Is it, though?

- Logic and objectivism is now viewed as the savior to the sociologically modern human. Institutions are constructed with multiple tiers, creating a bureaucracy that lives for rational purposes based upon fairness to all.

- Each problem, no matter how complex, has a rational answer (The Rube Goldberg Solution). We end up applying our logic to social problems, creating, for example courts, which fit subjective features into an objective decision-making process. One person is granted the opportunity to make rational decisions based upon previous, wise individuals who made similar decisions based upon similar arguments (common law).

- We try to solve social problems with rational, logically derived answers that have no business being resolved logically. The quintessential "rational" debate is, for example, about abortion. There is no rational answer, but merely an irrational value. It is people with values who try to apply rational arguments to support their views. It becomes unproductive.

## Period of the modern sociological human (post-AD 1900)

The implied consent of all humans is now necessary to perform basic tasks of daily living and maintaining personal sustenance for each individual. This allows interests of society to control us. The interconnectedness is so great that the consumers receiving products from the producers receive little if any benefit from those products; the producers receive virtually all the benefit.

## Sociologically modern human

As humans utilized our communication skills more effectively, the asocial being was gradually replaced by the social being. The individual that flourished was the one who could communicate more effectively and utilize the knowledge and skill of those around us to conquer natural problems. The social being came about early in human existence (at least 2.5 million years ago with the development of stone tools). Our prominence and eventual dominance as a species arose, however, as a result of our abilities to catalogue information, use group techniques to conquer natural problems, and develop culture to create the memes that would archive, transmit, and promote useful information for our survival: hence, the sociologically modern human.

- Resources are now pouring in to supporting arguments lacking a rational basis or foundation. Religious support is a classic example of where the US constitution protects the right to worship anything or anyone no matter how irrational. The end result is a host of institutions that support rarely understood values as a hidden meaning behind the growth of society. We blindly accept values because we think they are rationally derived.

## 20th Century: A Century of Logic

The application of logic is still a valuable part of humanity's growth during the 20th century, but as humanity's ICQ/ITQ grow larger, logic becomes less valuable to all of us. Still, in this decade, we make massive advances based upon our abilities to think rationally.

- Logic can and will advance our standard of living, as proven by the United States. No other country is as successful at applying logic to the social realm as the United States and its constitution.

- The United States, which has amassed the greatest wealth in history, has the greatest educational system. Educating all people, not just a privileged minority, to think logically is massively successful.

- At its height in the 1960s, the United States had the highest proportion of advanced degree holders in the population and the highest literacy rate in the world.

- Growth in this rational and rapid process of educating the general population was profound. In 1969, 77.1 percent graduated from high school compared to 2 percent in 1870.

- The United States was at, or near the top of, any country in the world in enrolling its population in post-secondary education (70.1 percent) and achieving the most years of formal education (13.3 years) for people 25 to 64 years of age.

## Spread of Ideas Becomes Exponentially More Rapid

While the United States and Europe are leading the world into a rationally supported existence, the growth of ideas rises exponentially. As individuals freely exchange ideas, rational thought continues to generate profound successes. A gradual but exponential growth in communications assists the exchange of ideas, but on the other hand, it allows irrational emotions and illogical arguments to be perpetuated by the population at large.

- Telephones and newspapers in the first quarter of the century dominate the fastest form of communications. Mass distribution of information takes days not hours. Reporters must write about events from a centralized location with editing, printing, and physical distribution of the newspapers. Telephones are regional, but cannot distribute information to large numbers of people quickly.

- Radio now dominates the second quarter of the century, as immediate communications to large masses of people is possible. People must still talk about events from a centralized location.

- Television in the third quarter of the century allows events to be seen and experienced by the masses in real time. Editing is minimized, but still present.

- The Internet in the fourth quarter of the century allows real events and ideas to be shared without editing from a centralized location. Raw reality is experienced on both a real basis and can be distorted by proponents of any debate on any issue no matter how illogical.

## Application of Logic

Logic can be applied to problem-solving in many ways. It is particularly effective solving inanimate problems. Logic cannot be applied as effectively for social situations. The types of problems logic is applied to are as follows:

- **The Good: Application of Logic on the Inanimate** Usually effective in problem solving.

- **The Benign: Benevolent Application of Logic on the Animate** Most of the time it serves useful functions to create cohesion, but there is an illusion of success.

- **The Bad: Malevolent Application of Logic on the Animate** The use of logic by individuals to justify social standing, irrational arguments, or manipulate social conditions and institutions is usually bad. It is an illusion and misapplication of resources. It eventually leads to war and human death.

## The Good: Application of Logic on the Inanimate

Since the beginning of the 20th century, using logic to resolve problems has been undoubtedly a success. Few would question that the scientific method has been a fundamental tool that humans have used to advance our standard of living. Why such an exponential growth of its use in the 20th century?

## Benevolence

Occurs when the self-regulating organism can *knowingly* produce a greater good for its self-regulating environment by also creating a better environment for the survival of other self-regulating organisms. It chooses to respect and even help those organisms to further its own survival. Self-regulating organisms realize that survival strategies for its internal homeostasis are dependent upon and optimized by group cooperation.

## Animate

Any living organism that has the ability to self-regulate its internal homeostasis and therefore put its own homeostasis ahead of the external environment surrounding itself. The more sophisticated these mechanisms' ability to self-regulate and create a better ability for self-survival, the more animate this organism is and the greater its ability to create unwanted, and perhaps unintended, consequences for other surrounding self-regulating organisms.

## Malevolence

Occurs when the self-regulating organism has the ability to *knowingly* produce a greater good for its self-regulating environment at the expense of other self regulating organisms. It chooses to allow this to occur.

- The synergy of discovery was nothing short of miraculous when concerning the inanimate. Interconnectedness allowed these ideas to spread more effectively and the efficiency of archiving the data became exponentially greater.

- As discovery advances, more cooperation and more resources are needed to solve problems. As knowledge increases, more archiving is needed, thus producing specialists who know about their fields. These specialists required resources to promote study in their fields.

- Discovery began to require several decisions. Do we expend resources (or not) to learn more? Will our discoveries lead to better living standards? Do we need to understand what to discover? More importantly, is humanity even capable of fully understanding why we are studying something, as scientists must use funds advanced by nonscientists.

- Resource allocation and not imagination eventually becomes the limiting factor to discovery. The merging of nonscientists with scientists in logical problem-solving then makes for the bureaucratization of science. The rational scientist must lobby for his ideas to confirm his hypothesis.

## Changes in the Structure of Our Discoveries in the 20th Century

As the century progresses, three periods of technological discoveries are apparent:

- **First third of the century:** Serendipitous discoveries predominate. The "wildcat" scientist who toils and makes remarkable discoveries with relatively small amounts of capital dominates this period. Discovery is a luxury, and failure was inconsequential to society. Examples include the following: Thomas Edison and the light bulb; Albert Einstein and relativity; William Röntgen and the x-ray; Wright Brothers and controlled flight; and Karl Benz and the internal combustion engine.

- **Second third of the century:** Bureaucratic discoveries occur in which large amounts of capital are needed to better understand our world. Entire paradigms need to be funded. Researchers learn their craft among their colleagues with similar detailed knowledge. Success is achieved but at larger expense. NIH is created in 1930 for medical research and 16 national laboratories are created in 1931 for physical science research. There is no clear inventor but always "teams" of inventors. Discovery is a critical tool, and failure is now problematic. Examples include the Manhattan Project, Quantum Mechanics, Framingham Heart Study, the transistor, the television, and the Apollo Project.

- **Last third of the century:** Planned discoveries become ever so important. Huge amounts of capital are needed for even the most rudimentary discoveries. We believe we can discover something based upon our current understanding. We are merely conducting science to placate investors and grantors—not for the benefits the discoveries may bring. Costs dramatically skyrocket, and if the discovery is not successful, the process is deemed a failure. Discovery is a necessity; failure is not an option. Examples include the Space Shuttle, Internet, Human Genome Project, and the war on cancer.

# The Benign: Benevolent Application of Logic on the Animate

Highly persuasive arguments using logic in the physical realm now become increasingly applied to the social realm. The end result is that most applications are of little value to the social scientist trying to solve problems in our world today.

- With tremendous successes in the inanimate, applications of the scientific method become bastardized to the social realm. Abortion, the stock market, gambling, and religion are examples of individuals trying to understand the social realm through the misapplication of logic.

- We convince ourselves through detailed charts, graphs, and numbers that we can predict the future of a sociological phenomenon. In reality, because of our high ICQ/ITQ we are creating self-fulfilling prophesies. We think we are advancing scientifically in the animate realm, but it is an illusion. Our increasing ICQ/ITQ and the quick feedback mechanisms of our current world make scientific study and prediction of future events a growing impossibility.

- This misapplication of logic is fairly benign if applied by an individual who is thinking of the greater good (benevolent application). These people are mainly thinking of ways to extract wealth from society and not contributing to wealth creation. The day trader is a classic example. Society can exist with this type of misapplication, but it is a drain on its resources.

- When a sociologist, psychologist or economist tells us we should act a certain way, we do so simply because we think it is an immutable law. These scientists' predictions come true and they become "experts" on human behavior simply because their expertise is accepted as a given without critical evaluation. They merely describe social behavior but cannot predict it. We believe them and they believe in themselves to help society and help avoid the unpredictability of human behavior.

## Recent Attempts to Scientifically Understand the Animate

It is not totally clear whether science is ever successful in the social realm. In less interconnected environments, its success is of less relevance. As our interconnectedness increases, our science breaks down. Recent attempts to understand the social realm were made by the following philosophers:

- **August Comte:** In the 19th century, he had a unidirectional positivist view of behavior (we commit acts because of predetermined causes which control us). Behavior is one way (from genes or the environment to us). We can find the cause to any behavior and predict it and tame it eventually through scientific understanding.

- **Robert Merton:** In the first half of the 20th century, he argued behavior was determined by feedback mechanisms with the environment. These he called self-fulfilling prophecies (we react to our environment when we study it). He argued we need to take into account our effects on the environment.

- **Karl Popper:** He argued in the middle of the 20th century that behavior was impossible to control because it involved feedback mechanisms that made scientific study of those phenomena an impossibility. He called this the theory of reflexivity.

- **Anthony Giddens:** He argues in the late 20th century that social environments are structural and not completely unpredictable. He called this structuration theory. Our reactions to these environments become somewhat predictable. We create social structure that we can react to and go back and forth in our attempts to scientifically predict our social structure (called the double hermeneutic). Giddens was more hopeful than Popper that human behavior could be predicted based upon this double hermeneutic. Giddens doesn't take into account the increasing interconnectedness that makes structure less relevant to future behavior.

- **Pierre Bourdieu:** He argues in the late 20th century that there is a structure to our changes, based upon previous knowledge or symbols ("symbolic or cultural capital"). We can study an evolution to our society. He calls this genetic structuralism. He attempts to unite the subjective ("habitus") and objective ("field") into one meaning. He is confident that reflexivity can be overcome by the academic awareness of one's own bias or "habitus." With increasing interconnectedness, it is not clear whether this true interaction can ever be understood in the future.

## Hopeless Application of Scientific Knowledge on the Animate

In spite of the attempts of several individuals to lay out an ability to study human behavior, we still are left with the problems inherent in behavioral freedom now and into our future. We could have the most powerful computers studying a near infinite number of variables and we still wouldn't be able to predict the future behavior of complex beings. Why?

- "Freshly minted" history is always being made which has the greatest influence on behavior. How does one objectively study "freshly minted" history?

- With the increasing ICQ/ITQ, this hyperdynamism is only getting more difficult to study, not less. The more successful we are as a species the greater the interconnectedness and the greater the increase in behavioral entropy.

- The "laws" of the past do not apply to the future because of the short memory of the biological organism and its reaction to its infinitely unique environment.

- Acceptance of social theory is subject to manipulation—far more than physical theories. Often the theory with the most resources wins the debate, not the theory with the most intrinsic value to our species.

- The more general or macroscopic the theory, the less helpful the theory, but the less it is subject to manipulation and bias; the more microscopic the theory, the more helpful, but more subject to manipulation and bias.

- Karl Popper is correct. To predict the future is hopeless in a biological world:

   "The sum total of the conditions—internal and external—under which we repeat a certain experiment on one and the same organism cannot therefore be sufficiently similar for us to speak of a real repetition. For even an exact repetition of environmental conditions would be combined with new internal conditions in the organism; the organism learns by experience."

## The Bad: Malevolent Application of Logic on the Animate

The most feared misuse of logic is for the express use of individuals to justify actions that allow them to achieve benefit at the expense of others. Malevolence is an increasingly dangerous problem in the sociologically modern human as explained below:

- Malevolence is the seeking of resources to better one's internal homeostasis while *knowingly* having a negative effect on the homeostasis of other beings around oneself.

- With the rise of ICQ/ITQ, rising standards of living, declining resource base, and disparities in wealth comes the rise of malevolence, which is unavoidable.

- As long as resources remain plentiful, benevolent application of logic remains predominant; if resources are scarce, malevolence rises.

- With the paradoxical rise of individual power to affect the remainder of society, the few who are malevolent can have a devastating effect on the Supercivilization. In the short term, these malevolent people may benefit, but in the long term because of the exponentially rising interconnectedness, it will be catastrophic for everyone, including the malevolent people themselves.

- With the rapid rise of micro-technology and the precipitously decreasing costs to build those technologies, one can blackmail the entire Supercivilization relatively easily compared to the past. This is highly problematic for every human alive.

# The Realization of Malevolence: It Becomes Valued

Prior to the fundamentally profound drop in resources, malevolence becomes valued, as those receiving benefit seem, in the short term, to greatly prosper. Those receiving benefit can also manipulate our culture to skew opinions toward their self-assured, righteous, deserved place. Unfortunately, it is the sudden rise, followed by a massive catastrophic fall that appears imminent. Here is what is happening today in our culture:

- Our basic proclivity toward benevolence and malevolence is not genetic, social, or physical in nature. It is all three factors and can never be isolated in a causative fashion; it is holistically derived and cannot be disentangled or isolated as an environmental or genetic trait.

- We now view the world as one in which "I" can control others. "I" comes first before others because of this implicit power we all possess today.

- Malevolence used effectively is "prized" as cunning, shrewd, or

## Paradox of individual power of society

Even though a single human has never been so seemingly inconsequential (one of 7 billion people), he and/or she has never had such an ability to affect the lives of more people than today. Just one individual in the world today can wield more power than at any other time in human history.

## Benevolence/malevolence paradox

The more empowered we become, the more likely we are to use that power to create benefit for ourselves and the more likely it will inspire others and empower others, thereby really making us less powerful. The closer we are to others and the less we fight natural problems (the higher the ICQ/ITQ) the more likely this paradox inspires us to cooperate. Malevolence ultimately occurs because of benevolence and vice versa. Benevolence and malevolence predominate in society at differing times based upon our overwhelming challenge at that period in time: natural or human-induced problems. We become benevolent when our challenges are primarily natural and turn malevolent when we succeed at natural problem solving and our challenges become human-induced.

simply smart business utilizing the existing norms and laws to achieve success.

- Because of the interconnectedness of economic markets, we find that financial power over others when we threaten supply lines—which causes a domino effect on other areas—can ingratiate us. We naturally feel empowered.

- With the rise of free time from the wealth we create (discretionary problem-solving), we can now think of ways to control world markets for our benefit. We do not directly feel the impact of our threats on others, and so our malevolence is disguised, even dismissed as being "natural or genetic" by powerful interests who benefit from the malevolence.

- The rise of rational thought and logic removes religion as an irrational conduit that previously promoted benevolence. As our irrationality gets stripped by our growing culture of logic and rationalism, suddenly the social glue that holds us together quickly vanishes once our resource base drops. The end result is a futile, malevolent growth in society that can no longer be controlled. Every man, woman, and child is for him or her self. Hence, we have the benevolence/malevolence paradox.

## Problem-Solving in a Malevolent, Irrational World

Clearly, our ability to focus and solve problems we *wish to solve* is simply spectacular in the 20th century. Landing on the moon is a classic example. Inanimate problems we choose to solve and which are the easiest to resolve, can be solved. Yet, some are not. Why? Even more discouraging is that the animate problems of humanity are light years more difficult to resolve. Why?

- Many large, overarching problems never are resolved and distractions are created (pseudosolutions) to manipulate the minds of individuals into thinking the most important problems are being resolved. Climate change is the classic example of this problem type.

- The small, trivial problems are resolved simply because vested interests want us to solve those problems to give us all a sense of accomplishment and keep the real problems off the agenda.

- With huge debates in the public realm, little gets accomplished other than creating compromises that solve nothing.

- The best solutions for society are not chosen; rather the least offensive solution is chosen, especially in a liberal democracy (enter political correctness). When interconnectedness is so great, a liberal democracy, while offering the greatest fairness for accepting an idea, is subject to mass manipulation.

- Real solutions to social problems require winners and losers for utilitarian gains. The progress is so slow that a liberal democracy cannot possibly keep up with the hyperdynamism of a high ICQ/ITQ environment and the problems it generates.

- The higher the ICQ/ITQ the more effective the vested interests are at controlling the agenda and hence controlling the minds of all individuals in society. The larger the resource disparities the less likely vested interests with the most resources will be convinced to spend the necessary resources to resolve overarching problems.

## Difficulty in Problem-Solving in the Social Environment: Easiest to Most Difficult

I now cite six examples of how ideas and attempts at problem solving have been affected by vested interests. I start with the problems with the least controversy and the fewest vested interests opposed to its solution and end with the most controversial problem with the most vested interests in opposition.

### 1. Hitler, E=MC², and the Manhattan Project

It took just six years to invent the most devastating weapon in human history. The fear of Adolph Hitler and the Nazis promulgated a crash program, based upon the theories of Albert Einstein and the conversion of mass into energy, resulted in the development of the atomic bomb. Several key factors catapulted the development of this weapon.

- **Desperation:** All Americans agreed that Hitler's plans were insane. There was genuine fear that he could gain control of this weapon (perhaps the biggest driving factor in its development) by inventing it first.

- **Inanimate problem:** The nature of the solution involved theoretical physics and the laws of mathematics, which are relatively easy to resolve.

- **Esoteric nature:** The common individual had no clue as to what theoretical physics was or how it could be applied to the human condition. The project could be hidden from public discussion because of its secretive nature in the war effort.

- **Unlimited budget:** Scientists were given the green light on spending. This project would be completed regardless of cost.

- **Failure not an option:** No one was allowed to fail, because failure could mean the end to Western liberal democracy and even human civilization.

## 2. Darwin's Theory of Natural Selection and Educational Instruction

One hundred and fifty-four years after Charles Darwin first presented his theory of natural selection, his work still has not been fully accepted by the general population. It took several decades before even the scientific establishment accepted Darwin's concepts. Today, 48 percent of Americans and an unbelievable 16 percent of biology teachers still do not embrace Darwin's theory of evolution. Why does this differ so much from Einstein's theory of relativity?

- **A biological principle:** Darwin's theory isn't a law because it involves biological organisms. Testing involving biological organisms is fraught with so much more complexity than experiments in the inanimate world. As a result of these biological complexities, evidence had to trickle in to support the theory.

- **Conflicted with values of society at large:** One could not continue with a belief system and adopt a scientific principle in contradiction to that belief system without creating conflict. Long established values over thousands of years were eliminated with one's writing of the pen. A major irrational paradigm was threatened.

- **No lives at stake:** Nothing about Darwin's theory or its fundamental underlying principle was life-threatening.

- **Minimal budget to study:** Funding research to confirm Darwin's theory was always a challenge. Scientists trying to confirm Darwin's theory were often ostracized. Funding even from the government was slowed by interests opposed to natural selection.

## 3. Racism and the Civil Rights Movement

It took 246 years from the time slavery was first introduced into the United States until it was officially outlawed (and which to date, still exists de facto in some areas of the country). In spite of Judeo-Christian ethics, white Americans subjected African Americans to a barbaric existence. Why did a country founded on principles of liberties and freedoms continue for so long to promote this inhumane, racial bigotry?

- **Economic muscle behind its continued existence:** Those holding power in society would not allow slavery to disappear. Once a powerful economic force opposes the resolution of a problem, that problem rarely is resolved in a timely fashion no matter how unfair or inhumane. Congress was basically bribed by powerful interests to keep the status quo for over 75 years after the Constitution was signed.

- **Paradigm intransigence:** So many assumptions (wrongly espoused) about our biological nature as a species fought common sense. As we had little scientific understanding of our biology, we could justify this barbaric treatment quite easily. It wasn't until our scientific community during the 20th century confirmed (mainly through genetics) the biologically homogeneous nature of humans was this overarching paradigm extinguished.

- **Institutional indoctrination:** Every institution in this country was indoctrinated with this paradigm, which meant that immense social engineering was required to change it. This social engineering takes decades to centuries, regardless of the validity of the paradigm itself.

## 4. Lung Cancer and Tobacco

In spite of the number of deaths last century (100 million) and those projected for this century (1 billion at current rates), we continue to allow smoking to occur. And this unfortunate habit is still growing worldwide. Thirty-three percent of all adult men currently smoke worldwide. The rate of new smokers is growing at a 3.4 percent per year rate in the developing world. Tobacco kills half its users. Why is smoking still so prevalent?

- **Economic muscle:** Tobacco spent $125 million, for example, defeating the McCain tobacco control bill in 1998. There is little opposition to tobacco and its powerful economic position. The tobacco industry spends $12.8 billion in advertising every year.

- **International problem:** This problem requires universal cooperation of all countries—something that is lacking today. Few laws have been instituted in the developing world because of powerful tobacco lobbying and outright bribery.

- **Addictive nature of the product:** Once individuals become addicted to this product, it is difficult to quit. This type of addiction is so profound that smokers themselves are often opposed to laws that will eliminate its use.

- **Cultural context is powerful:** Tobacco has been a powerful symbol of sexuality in the cinema and is still associated with sophistication, defiance, and success. We were all indoctrinated effectively through one hundred years of powerful advertising with the idea that cigarette smoking is acceptable, even desirable, in advanced societies.

## 5. Illegal Drug Use in Society

Drug use is an ongoing problem with 147 million regular users of marijuana and 50 million regular users of cocaine, heroin, and methamphetamines worldwide. This is an international problem in which all countries are complicit. Costs to society are staggering. This problem alone costs the United States $193 billion annually in indirect expenses to society. If drugs are so universally bad, why are they still present in such great amounts?

- **Interdiction requires international cooperation:** All of these drugs are mostly cultivated or produced in Third World countries and are consumed by First World countries, particularly the United States. One country cannot resolve this problem alone. Drug trafficking is a huge business that requires multiple nations to intervene at key points.

- **Addictive nature of substances:** These are addictive substances, and the end user serves as an ongoing, reliable source for demand.

- **Growers desperate for cash:** Individuals who cultivate the crops necessary for drug production have minimal choice. These crops result in excessive profits that would otherwise be lost in the production of other far less valuable crops.

- **Conflicting views on drugs:** Some areas of the world allow drug use and others take a dim view. Some view it as a medical problem, and others view it as a moral weakness. Some areas have strict laws, while other areas have minimal laws. Some countries make it a priority, while other countries have virtually no enforcement resources.

## 6. Arab-Israeli Conflict

This is by far the most difficult problem to resolve: the purely irrational argument that has no rational resolution. Throughout the entire 20th century the land on the shore of the eastern Mediterranean has been a hotbed of violence and hostility that is unresolved to date. After three major wars and numerous skirmishes killing thousands of people over the last 65 years, this conflict is no closer to resolution than it was at the start of the 20th century. Why?

- **Both sides argue from an irrational founding assumption:** Both Israel and the Palestinians are making arguments that have no rational basis. This is the most difficult argument to win. When each side is embedded in an irrational premise, no amount of rational argument will ever win. Individuals forsake reality for a higher cause (see Prion of Anthropocentricity in chapter 11) because of thousand year-old scriptures (Tanakh and Koran) and previous acts of hatred based upon cultural differences.

- **Emotions are running high:** Most diplomats on both sides argue that the stakes are high. Violent interactions have been egregious. Most Israelis and Palestinians have either lost someone or know someone who has lost a loved one because of this conflict. The livelihood of current generations is dependent upon a resolution, as families have had to endure great hardship (move to new locations, combat terrorists, etc) to accommodate the fallout from this conflict.

- **The entire world's economy is at stake:** Because of the nature of fossil fuel use, this conflict has a major impact on all human beings. The 1973 oil embargo by OPEC was instituted because of the fallout. The flow of oil through the Suez Canal is always at a high threat level. The Cold War also made this conflict a potential catalyst for world war as the Soviets generally would side with the Palestinians and the United States would side with Israel.

- **It is an international problem with no leadership:** No clear governing body has the power to resolve or even make decisions about this conflict. While the United Nations attempts to resolve this problem, no clear answer is apparent. Both sides can elect to disregard international sanctions, if they so choose.

- **Generations of traditions and paradigms are difficult to shake loose:** Cultures have been created and paradigms have been firmly entrenched for over a thousand years to support various arguments. To resolve these disputes, tradition would have to be usurped.

- **Military escalation is problematic:** Just one misunderstanding can lead to annihilation. Both sides are backed by a superpower who can unleash horrifically deadly weapons on humanity. Both sides are also heavily armed to make this problem far more dramatic than it needs to be.

# Manifestations of Malevolence: Stoppable?

Many believe this malevolence is unstoppable and is an inevitable part of who we are as human beings. I argue it is a manifestation of our biosociophysical reality today. Human behavior adheres to no laws. We can change this reality if we realize it is not inevitable.

To understand malevolence today, we must look at its most dangerous manifestations and its causes. Individual malevolence is socially manifested primarily in two ways:

- **Disorganized malevolence:** This is manifested through existing institutions within society. Corporate greed and crime are two basic examples. In the past, disorganized malevolence remained localized because of the low interconnectedness and limited technology. Today, it is still of minimal consequence, as those who are malevolent usually want to work within society. They do not want to change it or even destroy it.

- **Malevolent movements:** In the past, these movements were slow and lumbering as interconnectedness was low, technology limited, and huge numbers of individuals were needed to bring these movements to fruition. Because coordination was needed, these movements had large impacts locally but limited impacts globally. Three stages of malevolent conflict are manifested over the century:

  » **World wars:** Manifested through large institutional support, treaties were formed to protect the world from rogue nations. But they were problematic. These treaties discouraged small skirmishes by creating a profound fear of escalation; however, the fear of escalation encouraged those immoral leaders to use fear as a tool.

  » **Regional conflicts and the Cold War:** A bipolar Hegelian world of Soviet versus American nations became reality in the middle of the 20th century. The huge armaments were comfortably in the hands of rational and moral bureaucracies on many levels. War could be seen as mutually assured destruction and was not winnable. Weapons of mass destruction were still difficult to create and required capital that only a nation could garner.

  » **The War on Terror:** In the last three decades of the 20th century, blackmail can now be achieved by small malevolent groups who know the effects their mischief can cause and the results they can achieve. The increased interconnectedness is a fundamental reason for their success. While improved technology allows terrorists to achieve more dangerous acts, the mere fact that they can propagandize their views through a willing and able press makes them exponentially more effective.

# Final Mortality Statistics of the 20th Century

To further demonstrate the rise of human-induced problems leading to the transition from the Second to the Third Biosociophysical Era of Humanity is the analysis of mortality statistics during the 20th century. This is the first century we have accurately estimated the average life span and the causes of death. Several conclusions can be made about causation of death during the 20th century:

- At the start of the century people die mainly of little-understood natural events.

- As the century progresses we have a remarkable increase in our understanding of disease and can thus create major solutions to potentially resolve these diseases.

- We also have an increasing inability to resolve human disease, catastrophes, and accidents through human cooperation.

- The resolution of these human-induced problems is difficult because of the following:

  » **The rapid rise of malevolence:** Resolution of human-induced deaths requires unprecedented cooperation because of the types of problems (such as communicable disease) being resolved. We choose not to resolve these problems because of our fundamental belief that health care is a meritorious pursuit and is not a right for every human. One must earn the right to receive health care.

  » **The rapid rise of irrationality:** The application of our medical discoveries on the human population is fraught with the need to be rational. Irrationality is rising, and therefore, applying a rational pursuit to an irrational environment or population is fraught with inordinately difficult challenges. It only gets worse as the irrationality increases throughout the century.

  » **A limiting of our resources and their effective and efficient distribution:** As resource use spins out of control because of a free market that rewards the producer of the medical products and not necessarily the consumer, we start to hit upon limits of maximal resource use. Health care becomes a major problem. We cannot easily resolve these problems in the late 20th and early 21st century. Diseases are invented for the benefits of the producer, and dependence upon the medical-industrial complex becomes universal and unprecedented.

## Four Key Mortality Statistics 1900–2000

I examine four key mortality statistics as indicators of the sociologically modern period of the Second Biosociophysical Era of Humanity. These four demonstrate the sudden and explosive rise in the percentage of human deaths as caused by human-induced problems. The four statistics include the following:

- Substantial drop *initially* in years of potential life lost (YPLL) in the United States (Figures 3.1 and 3.2): This is perhaps a key objective indicator of our success with declining mortality. Prior to 1980 (before we kept adequate statistics of YPLL), proxy indicators (death rate, life expectancy, and infant mortality) reflect a steep drop. The most significant success in health care occurred in the first half of the century.

- Initial dramatic drop in diseases of natural origin (Figures 3.3 and 3.4): Naturally occurring diseases that are little understood simply dissipate to a minor role in death causation as the century progresses (author estimates only the top ten causes of death).

  » 1900: 93.2 percent natural; 6.8 percent human-induced

  » 1950: 80.2 percent natural; 19.8 percent human-induced

  » 1998: 45.7 percent natural; 54.3 percent human-induced

- Slower more sustained drop in YPLL in the United States: 1980 to 2010 (see Figure 3.5) saw slower but sustained drops in YPLL (at least 2.1 percent every five years) with an average of 5.3 percent (crude) and 6.1 (age-adjusted). Since 1980 a slow but steady decrease in this number reflects definite, but more limited success. This is because of the less successful application of health care on disease.

- Inability to promote resources for the dying (Figures 3.6 and 3.7). Those who need the resources the most receive the least. The amount of money spent per month of life saved becomes exponentially more expensive. Resources expended on the wealthy are adding little if any benefit to their health. A successful health care system is predicated on formulating internalized values of behavior, thereby promoting good health in individuals; it is not necessarily just healing the sick. That is one of the major the problems with our health care system today. Vested interests benefiting from the consumption of goods and services (the medical-industrial complex) simply control health care and who receives it. Prevention (that is, selling nothing) is discouraged because it encourages consuming less, not more. Prevention is unprofitable for the medical- industrial complex.

| Year | Deaths per 100,000 | Life Expectancy (years)** | Infant Mortality (per 1,000 live births)*** |
|---|---|---|---|
| 1900 | 1,719 | 48.2 | 110.8**** |
| 1910 | 1,468 | 50.2 | 96.5 |
| 1920 | 1,298 | 56.3 | 82.1 |
| 1930 | 1,132 | 59.1 | 60.1 |
| 1940 | 1,076 | 62.8 | 43.2 |
| 1950 | 963 | 66.3 | 26.8 |
| 1960 | 954 | 67.5 | 22.9 |
| 1970 | 945 | 67.9 | 17.8 |
| 1980 | 878 | 70.8 | 10.9 |
| 1990 | 864 | 72.7 | 7.6 |
| 2000 | 864* | 74.8 | 5.7 |

FIGURE 3.1   Death Rate, Life Expectancy, and Infant Mortality in the United States, 1900–2000

*1998 data
**White males
***Whites
*****1895

| Year | Deaths per 100,000 | Life Expectancy (years)** | Infant Mortality (per 1,000 live births)*** |
|------|--------------------|--------------------------|--------------------------------------------|
| 1910 | -14.6 | +4.1 | -12.9**** |
| 1920 | -24.5 | +16.8 | -25.9 |
| 1930 | -34.1 | +22.6 | -45.8 |
| 1940 | -37.4 | +30.3 | -61.0 |
| 1950 | -44.0 | +37.6 | -75.8 |
| 1960 | -44.5 | +40.0 | -79.3 |
| 1970 | -45.0 | +40.9 | -83.9 |
| 1980 | -48.9 | +46.9 | -90.2 |
| 1990 | -49.7 | +50.8 | -93.1 |
| 2000 | -49.7* | +55.2 | -94.9 |

FIGURE 3.2   Death Rate, Life Expectancy, and Infant Mortality in the United States, 1900–2000, and Percentage Change from the 1900 Level

\*1998 data    \*\*\*Whites
\*\*White males    \*\*\*\*Compared to 1895

**1900**

| Rank | Cause | Number | Deaths per 100,000 |
|------|-------|--------|--------------------|
| 1 | Pneumonia (all forms) and influenza | 40,362 | 202.2 |
| 2 | Tuberculosis (all forms) | 38,820 | 194.4 |
| 3 | Diarrhea, enteritis, and ulceration of the intestines | 28,491 | 142.7 |
| 4 | Diseases of the heart | 27,427 | 137.4 |
| 5 | Intracranial lesions of vascular origin | 21,353 | 106.9 |
| 6 | Nephritis (all forms) | 17,699 | 88.6 |
| 7 | All accidents | 14,429 | 72.3 |
| 8 | Cancer and other malignant tumors | 12,769 | 64.0 |
| 9 | Senility | 10,015 | 50.2 |
| 10 | Diphtheria | 8,056 | 40.3 |

FIGURE 3.3   Ten Leading Causes of Death in the United States in 1900, 1950, and 1998

The Supercivilization: Essential Concepts

**1950**

| Rank | Cause | Number | Deaths per 100,000 |
|------|-------|--------|--------------------|
| 1 | Diseases of the heart | 535,705 | 355.5 |
| 2 | Malignant neoplasms, including neoplasms of lymphatic and hematopoietic tissues | 210,733 | 139.8 |
| 3 | Vascular lesions affecting the central nervous system | 156,751 | 104.0 |
| 4 | Accidents | 91,249 | 60.6 |
|  | Motor vehicle accidents | 34,763 | 23.1 |
|  | All other accidents | 56,486 | 37.5 |
| 5 | Certain diseases of early infancy | 60,989 | 40.5 |
| 6 | Influenza and pneumonia, except pneumonia of the newborn | 47,120 | 31.3 |
| 7 | Tuberculosis (all forms) | 33,959 | 22.5 |
| 8 | General arteriosclerosis | 30,734 | 20.4 |
| 9 | Chronic and unspecified nephritis and other renal sclerosis | 24,677 | 16.4 |
| 10 | Diabetes mellitus | 24,419 | 16.2 |

**1998**

| Rank | Cause | Number | Deaths per 100,000 |
|------|-------|--------|--------------------|
| 1 | Diseases of the heart | 724,859 | 262.8 |
| 2 | Malignant neoplasms, including neoplasms of lymphatic and hematopoietic tissues | 541,532 | 200.3 |
| 3 | Cerebrovascular diseases | 158,448 | 58.6 |
| 4 | Chronic obstructive pulmonary diseases and allied conditions | 112,584 | 41.7 |
| 5 | Accidents and adverse effects | 97,835 | 36.2 |
|  | Motor vehicle accidents | 43,501 | 16.1 |
|  | All other accidents and adverse effects | 54,334 | 20.1 |
| 6 | Pneumonia and influenza | 91,871 | 34.0 |
| 7 | Diabetes mellitus | 64,751 | 24.0 |
| 8 | Suicide | 30,575 | 11.3 |
| 9 | Nephritis, nephrotic syndrome, and nephrosis | 26,182 | 9.7 |
| 10 | Chronic liver disease and cirrhosis | 25,192 | 9.3 |

FIGURE 3.3 (cont'd)    Ten Leading Causes of Death in the United States in 1900, 1950, and 1998

## 1900: Deaths per 100,000 population

| Rank | Cause | Natural | Human-Induced |
|------|-------|---------|---------------|
| 1 | Pneumonia (all forms) and influenza | 202 | 0 |
| 2 | Tuberculosis (all forms) | 194 | 0 |
| 3 | Diarrhea, enteritis, and ulceration of the intestines | 142 | 0 |
| 4 | Diseases of the heart | 137 | 0 |
| 5 | Intracranial lesions of vascular origin | 106 | 0 |
| 6 | Accidents | 0 | 72 |
| 7 | Nephritis | 64 | 0 |
| 8 | Cancer and other malignant tumors | 50 | 0 |
| 9 | Senility | 50 | 0 |
| 10 | Diphtheria | 40 | 0 |
| | **Totals** | **985** | **72** |
| | **Percentage of Top 10 Causes of Death** | **93.2** | **6.8** |

## 1950: Deaths per 100,000 population

| Rank | Cause | Natural | Human-Induced |
|------|-------|---------|---------------|
| 1 | Diseases of the heart | 305.0 | 50.0 |
| 2 | Malignant neoplasms, including neoplasms of lymphatic and hematopoietic tissues | 139.0 | 0 |
| 3 | Vascular lesions affecting the central nervous system | 104.0 | 0 |
| 4 | Accidents | 0 | 60.6 |
| 5 | Certain diseases of early infancy | 20.2 | 20.2 |
| 6 | Influenza and pneumonia, except pneumonia of the newborn | 31.3 | 0 |
| 7 | Tuberculosis (all forms) | 11.3 | 11.3 |
| 8 | General arteriosclerosis | 15.0 | 5.4 |
| 9 | Chronic and unspecified nephritis and other renal sclerosis | 8.2 | 8.2 |
| 10 | Diabetes mellitus | 12.0 | 4.2 |
| | **Totals** | **646.0** | **159.9** |
| | **Percentage of Top 10 Causes of Death** | **80.2** | **19.8** |

FIGURE 3.4   Breakdown of Natural vs. Human-Induced Causes of Death in the United States in 1900, 1950, and 1998 (Estimated)[1]

The Supercivilization: Essential Concepts

## 1998: Deaths per 100,000 population

| Rank | Cause | Natural | Human-Induced |
|------|-------|---------|---------------|
| 1 | Diseases of the heart | 130.1 | 134.1 |
| 2 | Malignant neoplasms, including neoplasms of the lymphatic and hematopoietic tissues | 100.2 | 100.2 |
| 3 | Cerebrovascular diseases | 40.6 | 18.0 |
| 4 | Chronic obstructive pulmonary diseases and allied conditions | 0 | 41.7 |
| 5 | Accidents and adverse effects | 0 | 36.2 |
| 6 | Pneumonia and influenza | 24.0 | 10.0 |
| 7 | Diabetes mellitus | 12.0 | 12.0 |
| 8 | Suicide | 0 | 11.3 |
| 9 | Nephritis, nephrotic syndrome, and nephrosis | 4.6 | 4.6 |
| 10 | Chronic liver disease and cirrhosis | 3.0 | 6.3 |
| | **Totals** | **314.5** | **374.4** |
| | **Percentage of Top 10 Causes of Death** | **45.7** | **54.3** |

FIGURE 3.4 (cont'd)   Breakdown of Natural vs. Human-Induced Causes of Death in the United States in 1900, 1950, and 1998 (Estimated)[1]

[1]   The author has estimated the percentages of deaths attributable to human factors and natural factors (out of human control) based upon contemporaneous knowledge of each disease process.

| Year | Crude | % Change | Age Adjusted | % Change |
|---|---|---|---|---|
| 1980 | 10,268 | – | 10,448 | – |
| 1985 | 9,255 | -9.9 | – | – |
| 1990 | 8,997 | -12.4 | 9,086 | -13.0 |
| 1995 | 8,596 | -16.3 | 8,626 | -17.4 |
| 2000 | 7,529 | -26.7 | 8,626 | -27.9 |
| 2005 | 7,490 | -27.1 | – | -30.0 |
| 2010 | 6,981 | -32.0 | 6,643 | -36.4 |

FIGURE 3.5   Years of Potential Life Lost before Age 75 per 100,000 Population from 1980 to 2010 and Percentage Change from 1980 Level in the United States

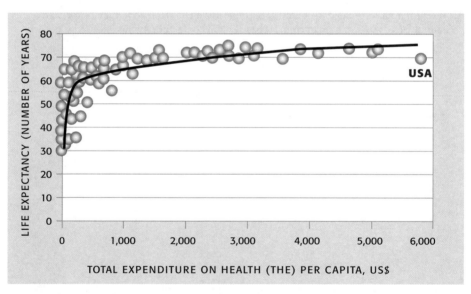

FIGURE 3.6   Life Expectancy vs. Total Expenditure on Health in Major Countries of the World (2003)
*Note that a plateau effect on resource procurement occurs.*

The Supercivilization: Essential Concepts

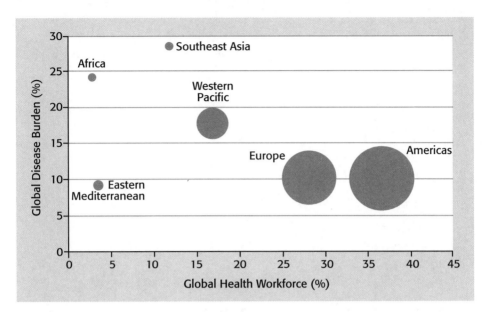

**FIGURE 3.7** Global Distribution of Health Workforce by Level of Expenditure and Disease Burden in Six WHO Regions.

Chapter 4

# Third Era of Humanity: Totally Human Dependent
## (POST-AD 2000)

"The spread of information will not necessarily encourage stability. Johannes Gutenberg's invention of movable type in the mid-fifteenth-century led not only to the Reformation but to the religious wars that followed it, as the sudden proliferation of texts spurred doctrinal controversies and awakened long-dormant grievances."

—*Robert D. Kaplan, author of* Warrior Politics

## Congruence Between Individual Success and Societal Success: Forever?

When humans fought nature-induced problems in their primal past, it required group cooperation. As humans accumulated goods and services, individuals learned to obtain these goods and services from others. By the time humans reached the 21st century, most success for individuals comes at the expense of others' hard work. The relationship of individual success versus societal success in the three eras is as follows:

- **First biosociophysical era:** individual success nearly always meant group success

- **Second biosociophysical era:** individual success sometimes meant group success

- **Third biosociophysical era:** individual success rarely means group success

## Third Era Now Requires Several Steps to Confirm a Discovery or Solution

The sociological human now is merely one person in a sea of people who must work together to solve problems. It is impossible for individuals to solve problems without the help of others. Socialization is mandatory. In order to solve any significant problems, lobbying must take place through six basic steps which takes significant time, energy, and capital:

1. Theoretical justification

2. Academic acknowledgment

3. Secular realization

4. Secular acknowledgment

5. Capital dispensation

6. Successful implementation

## The Golden Hour

In emergency medicine, the Golden Hour is defined as the period of time until a surgeon lays a hand on a patient who is dying of a significant trauma. Nothing matters except for surgery. All the efforts by a team of people make no difference if the one and only treatment—emergency surgery—isn't performed in a timely fashion. Today's Supercivilization is a dying trauma patient as categorized by the following:

- The Supercivilization is a dying patient with the one major injury that requires complete and fundamental cooperation to resolve: $CO_2$ emissions and climate change.

- The Golden Hour started in the year 2000 and we have until 2040 to resolve our biggest problem, climate change, through the birth of the Supercivilization.

- Vested interests want us to focus on solutions that allow them to continue their profitable ways, but we need only one solution right now—a surgeon to operate on the Supercivilization. We must reduce $CO_2$ emissions by at least 85 percent from 1990 levels, which requires *major* life-sustaining surgery for the Supercivilization. A change of this nature must be radical and must be done immediately. Minor solutions, like voluntary restrictions of $CO_2$ emissions (or tetanus shots to use the medical metaphor) are irrelevant and are only feel-good solutions.

- Members of the Supercivilization are still in denial. We are providing oxygen, tetanus shots, normal saline, blood products, etc, thinking that is sufficient. It isn't. Still, if we don't stop $CO_2$ emissions in its tracks now—we and future generations are doomed.

## Major Challenges Now Facing Humanity

As this is a new biosociophysical era we are embarking on, it will be a time of great adjustment. We must first acknowledge that our greatest threat is ourselves. It means we must forge the solutions that deal with us and not the inanimate. New institutions must be created to match the hyperdynamism of a gigantic global existence I call the Supercivilization. For our survival, we must face three major issues:

- **United Nations population projection:** There is a 1.1 percent growth rate today with a projection of 9.2 billion people by 2050. Can this world sustain 9.2 billion people given our resource challenges? New technology would have to be invented to sustain our standard of living. How can we create this technology given the rise of social intransigence and the molasses of social change? The social intransigence is something we control; nature does not. We can use hyperdynamism to our advantage only if we put the right institutions in place.

- **Volatility of markets increasing:** This volatility reflects the emotions of a highly interconnected world along with resource declines. The dot-com, housing, and commodities boom and bust (bubbles) are current examples. Market volatility occurs when poor institutional oversight occurs during resource declines. To decrease volatility, we must create institutions that create more stability and allow for more efficient use of resources. This is a major worldwide challenge today.

- **Relative levels of terrorism have increased:** The 1960s saw terrorist fatalities number in the double digits; the 1970s through 1990s numbered in the triple digits; in the twenty-first century deaths were in the quadruple digits. In spite of this exponential escalation of terrorism, the direct threat of terrorism is still minor. Fewer people have died of terrorism this century than those who die from automobile accidents in a single year in the United States. Terrorism itself, however, is not the threat; it is the reaction to terrorism that is the problem. Steven Pinker claims, "We are living in the most peaceful times in our species existence." He may be correct. Yet, if things are so peaceful, then why worry about terrorism? Simply the paradox of individual power makes the Supercivilization extremely dangerous. Resonant social pathology (see chapter 10) will doom all of us, as the hyperdynamism of the Supercivilization will create synergistic consequences from the terrorism that cannot be easily controlled.

## Civilizations Have Failed Because of Four Factors

Jared Diamond has studied the failure of civilizations and has listed three major factors that have contributed to the downfall of all major civilizations. I add a fourth and most critical factor: unless there is social cohesion to promote a paradigm (or social prion) of "us", as opposed to "me", there becomes a disintegrating factor that makes individuals feel that the solution is to destroy others around him or her before standards of living are impacted. This desire to seek individual well-being rather than group cohesion and group solutions is the major culprit.

The four factors are listed below:

- **Overpopulation:** Resources can no longer support the densities required to survive at the standard of living that individuals enjoy through participation in that civilization.

- **Environmental destruction:** In maintaining high population densities, environmental destruction is the sacrificing factor that allows living standards to be maintained.

- **Resource depletion:** This is the end result of the human population growth that is unsustainable given our current standard of living.

- **Inability to form psychological bonds between citizens (the key factor):** Solutions to the above three variables can result either from self-sacrifice and cooperation or from individualistic tendencies. If no bond promotes self-sacrifice and group solutions, this fourth factor will be the underlying destructive variable. As we are now one Supercivilization with no place to go and no other options, the destructive potential of our die-off—billions of people instead of hundreds, thousands, or even millions—will be exponentially greater.

## Paradigm of the Supercivilization Must Be Instilled in All of Us

Our greatest challenge now is to instill a paradigm of bonding that makes our overarching existence our highest priority. If we are unsuccessful, we will probably see a die-off sometime this century. To be successful, I argue two major goals must be achieved and six major factors must be introduced to achieve these goals.

To instill this paradigm, we must achieve two goals:

- **Realign our institutions to promote this paradigm:** Without major institutions to support the Supercivilization, we are a sitting duck. Cultures will remain heterogeneous and solutions for most people will be seen as "destroying them," rather than looking at better solutions that protect all of us.

- **Continue to ensure that the standard of living improves for all humans:** Without continued improvement in the standard of living, we will see unrest and panic. People need assurances that the future will be better, otherwise cooperation will flounder.

Achieving these two goals depends on six major factors:

- **Adequate leadership:** Our leaders must realize that universal participation is far more important than the type of institutions or socioeconomic systems we choose. If dissent occurs, valuable resources become misdirected on irrational pursuits that are difficult to resolve. The current cultural mosaic gives us no bonds, which weakens participation and promotes discord.

- **Ensuring minimum standards of living and health care for all humans:** Giving all humans access to food, shelter, clothing, and health care through a centralized authority, such as a global government, is fundamental. Currently, resource disparities are massive and exemplified in four major areas:

  » Disparity in GDP per capita (Figures 4.1A and B, 4.2, and 4.3)

  » Disparity in life expectancy (Figure 4.4)

| REGION | YEAR | | | | | | | | | | | | |
|---|---|---|---|---|---|---|---|---|---|---|---|---|---|
| | AD 1 | 1000 | 1500 | 1600 | 1700 | 1820 | 1870 | 1900 | 1940 | 1960 | 1980 | 1990 | 2003 |
| Western Europe | 576 | 427 | 772 | 889 | 997 | 1,960 | 2,087 | 2,892 | 4,547 | 6,896 | 13,197 | 15,965 | 19,912 |
| Western Europe Offshoots | 400 | 400 | 400 | 400 | 476 | 1,202 | 2,419 | 4,015 | 6,838 | 10,961 | 18,060 | 22,345 | 28,039 |
| Eastern Europe | 412 | 400 | 496 | 548 | 606 | 683 | 937 | 1,438 | 1,969 | 3,070 | 5,786 | 5,440 | 6,476 |
| Former USSR | 400 | 400 | 499 | 552 | 610 | 688 | 943 | 1,237 | 2,144 | 3,945 | 6,427 | 6,890 | 5,397 |
| Latin America | 400 | 400 | 416 | 438 | 527 | 691 | 676 | 1,113 | 1,933 | 3,129 | 5,440 | 5,072 | 5,786 |
| Asia | 456 | 470 | 568 | 574 | 572 | 581 | 556 | 638 | 897 | 1,027 | 2,032 | 2,784 | 4,434 |
| Africa | 472 | 425 | 414 | 422 | 421 | 420 | 500 | 601 | 813 | 1,063 | 1,538 | 1,449 | 1,549 |
| World Average | 467 | 453 | 566 | 596 | 615 | 667 | 873 | 1,262 | 1,962 | 2,775 | 4,521 | 5,162 | 6,516 |

**FIGURE 4.1 A** Per Capita GDP in Major Regions over the Last 2,003 Years (Constant 1990 US Dollars)
*Note the growing disparities between regions.*

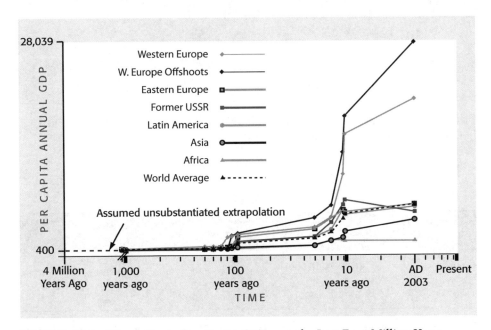

**FIGURE 4.1 B** Disparities in Per Capita GDP over the Last Four Million Years (Constant 1990 US Dollars)

» Disparity in infant mortality (Figure 4.4)

» Disparity in communications (Figure 4.5)

- **Limiting population growth:** Unlike the past, most population growth is now occurring in the poorest areas of Earth (Figure 4.6). The African population is projected to grow 80 percent by 2050, while Europe is projected to decrease by 14 percent. When minimum standards of living are met, the need to procreate declines. China has shown policies can be implemented successfully when population growth control is made a high priority.

- **Limiting resource utilization:** The rise of one resource, fossil fuels, has made the Supercivilization possible. Without this resource, other resources

| Rank | Range of Countries Per Capita GDP | Average Per Capita GDP | % GDP of Highest Quintile |
|------|------|------|------|
| 1st | (30,000–118,000) | 44,559 | – |
| 2nd | (11,900–29,600) | 18,222 | 40.9 |
| 3rd | (5,300–11,800) | 8,587 | 19.3 |
| 4th | (2,200–5,200) | 3,515 | 7.9 |
| 5th | (200–2,200) | 1,215 | 2.7 |

FIGURE 4.2 Average Per Capita GDP (US Dollars) of Countries in 2008, Ranked in Quintiles (229 Countries and Territories).

| Half | Range of Countries Per Capita GDP | Average Per Capita GDP | % GDP of Top Half |
|------|------|------|------|
| Top | (8,800–118,000) | 27,309 | – |
| Bottom | (200–8,600) | 3,292 | 12.1 |

FIGURE 4.3 Average Per Capita GDP (US Dollars) of Countries, Comparing Top to Bottom Half in 2008 (229 Countries and Territories)

The Supercivilization: Essential Concepts

| Countries[1] | Infant Mortality (Per 1,000 Live Births) | Rank[2] | Life Expectancy (Years) | Rank[3] |
|---|---|---|---|---|
| **Top 5** | | | | |
| Norway | 3.6 | 11 | 80.0 | 24 |
| Singapore | 2.3 | 1 | 82.0 | 4 |
| United States | 6.3 | 46 | 78.1 | 50 |
| Ireland | 5.1 | 37 | 78.2 | 47 |
| Switzerland | 4.2 | 16 | 80.9 | 11 |
| **Middle 5** | | | | |
| Colombia | 18.9 | 117 | 72.8 | 114 |
| Angola | 180.2 | 224 | 38.2 | 222 |
| Thailand | 17.6 | 108 | 72.6 | 109 |
| Peru | 28.6 | 147 | 70.7 | 138 |
| Dominican Republic | 26.0 | 142 | 73.7 | 99 |
| **Bottom 5** | | | | |
| Somalia | 109.2 | 219 | 49.6 | 207 |
| Liberia | 138.2 | 221 | 41.8 | 217 |
| Burundi | 59.6 | 187 | 52.1 | 201 |
| Congo, Dem. Republic of | 81.2 | 206 | 54.4 | 193 |
| Zimbabwe | 32.3 | 154 | 45.8 | 212 |

[1] 229 countries and territories
[2] 224 countries and territories
[3] 223 countries and territories

FIGURE 4.4  Per Capita GDP of Top, Middle, and Bottom 5 Countries and Territories vs. Infant Mortality and Life Expectancy in 2008 (Includes only Countries Over 3 Million in Population)

| | Regions | 1990 | 1995 | 2000 | 2005 | 2010 |
|---|---|---|---|---|---|---|
| **Cellular Subscribers per 1,000 People** | USA | 21.1 | 127 | 388 | 683 | 946 |
| | W. Europe | 9.1 | 60 | 634 | 930 | 1,008 |
| | Asia-Pacific | 0.4 | 7.1 | 71 | 230 | 379 |
| | Worldwide | 2.1 | 15.6 | 123 | 319 | 478 |
| **Internet Users per 1,000 People** | USA | 7.2 | 105 | 477 | 668 | 839 |
| | W. Europe | 0.5 | 22 | 244 | 535 | 788 |
| | Asia-Pacific | 0.03 | 1.2 | 34 | 116 | 193 |
| | Worldwide | 0.4 | 7.9 | 69 | 167 | 262 |
| **PCs in Use per 1,000 People** | USA | 192 | 321 | 628 | 778 | 932 |
| | W. Europe | 69 | 158 | 330 | 543 | 755 |
| | Asia-Pacific | 4.8 | 14.6 | 39 | 75 | 118 |
| | Worldwide | 18.6 | 40 | 87 | 140 | 201 |

**FIGURE 4.5**  Cell Phone Subscribers, Internet Users, and PCs in Use per 1,000 People Worldwide

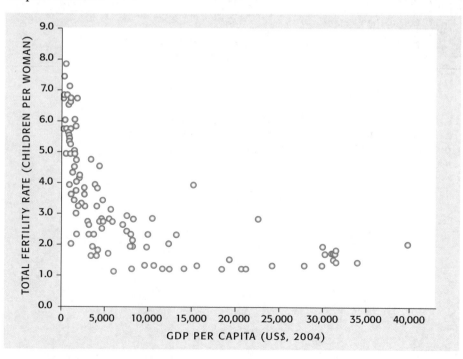

**FIGURE 4.6**  Total Fertility Rate vs. GDP Per Capita in 2004
*Limits: Countries with populations over 5 million (108 countries). No data available for Somalia.*

The Supercivilization: Essential Concepts

are simply impossible. We are no longer creating cheap fuels, which is leading to sluggish economic growth. Waste elimination is now beyond problematic. It is prohibitive. New technology must be developed, which will probably lead to greater energy costs.

- **Identifying our major problems:** During the media bombardment of the twenty-first century, we have a difficult time prioritizing our problems. We have too many decisions and too much discretion in dealing with our problems. We must discourage vested interests from trivializing these issues.

- **Solving our major problems:** Global problems must be resolved. However, regional problems remain the priority, thereby forcing long term global problems, like climate change, to languish. Capital must flow to all areas of the Earth and not remain regionalized. Our major problems are human-induced and vested interests are focusing on nature-induced problems to distract us from the very problems induced by those interests. The only solution to ensuring that capital flows to the areas that need it most, we need to formulate a global government. I suggest the name The United States of Mother Earth.

## United States of Mother Earth

This is my hypothetical name for a global government succeeding after the scaffolding of Project Alliance (see page 191) is removed. This will be formed officially in a self-imposed ten-year period and is modeled after the United States Constitution and the Bill of Rights. I am proposing this would be the only nation on Earth and would require voluntary ratification for its existence by all the world's current nation-states. It would include a Constitution with three traditional branches (legislative, executive, judicial) and a fourth named the health branch that would guarantee health care for all people based on a predetermined percentage of GDP, disbursed as doctors and public health officials deem necessary.

# II. Problems for the Supercivilization

"If you hear hoofbeats, think horses, not zebras."

—Every doctor on this planet

# Chapter 5

# The Model for Potential Annihilation

"It ain't what you don't know that gets you into trouble.
 It's what you know for sure that just ain't so."

—*Mark Twain*

# Supercivilization Self-Annihilation: What Are the Odds?

Human behavior cannot be predicted, and, therefore, predicting a self-annihilation of the Supercivilization is impossible. However, this doesn't preclude us from estimating the odds of its occurrence.

- Many make the assumption that since hominins have been around 4 million years, our odds of succumbing to an event of self-annihilation are too low to worry about.

- Others are fatalistic and believe human violence is inevitable. As there is nothing we can do about our aggressive behavior, they believe we will succumb to war or human-induced catastrophe.

Both assumptions are wrong. These are unique times with interconnectedness exponentially greater than at any time in the past.

Risk aversion depends not only on the odds of each event occurring, but on whether events are interdependent or not. How does the occurrence of one event affect the odds of other events occurring?

## Swiss-Cheese Model of Risk Aversion

To best estimate risk of a die-off, we must determine whether these catastrophic events are independent or interdependent. The Swiss-cheese model describes independent events that have no effect on each other.

- When holes in a piece of Swiss cheese form, they randomly occur, and the formation of a sightline depends strictly on the random nature of the bubbles forming.

- Each bubble has no effect on the formation of other bubbles.

- The thicker the piece of cheese (or the more systems in place to avoid risk), the less likely one is to see through the piece of cheese (or the less likely a catastrophic event can occur).

- This model is applicable to hypodynamic, independent events and mainly applicable to natural events.

- If trying to calculate odds of self-annihilation or anticipate future events, it is important to determine if the events are truly independent.

- These types of events occurred more often when environments were less animate and there was less reflexivity.

# Planetary-Formation Model of Risk Aversion

Without a firm understanding of the forces behind a system's function, amazement—even a proclivity to explain these occurrences through supernatural or godlike forces—overtakes us. It isn't until we have a full understanding of these forces that we soon discover that what seems incredibly unlikely becomes probable. This model can be described as follows:

- With eight planets in our solar system moving in the same direction and in the same plane, one might assume the odds are one in 1028 that these planets formed randomly like bubbles in a piece of Swiss cheese.

- If one understands that the formation of planets from a nebulae are more likely to form in a plane and moving in the same direction, the odds suddenly are not impossibly low but extraordinarily high to form a solar system like ours.

- The key to understanding risk is to determine the causal relationship between events. If the occurrence of one event influences the occurrence of other events, the odds of a series of events can flip to the other extreme.

Most of the animate world consists of interconnected feedback mechanisms making hyperdynamism a prerequisite for existence. It is this hyperdynamism that makes seemingly impossible events possible, even probable.

Our biggest mistake is that we and our leaders misapply risk calculation models by assuming everything is governed by the Swiss-cheese model, when it is really described by the planetary-formation model. As there is no history of this level of interconnectedness, no one can predict how likely a catastrophic event, such as self-annihilation, is to occur.

# Is Life Fragile? Or is it Remarkably Resilient?

One may think life is fragile because we see life only on Earth and nowhere else. This could make sense. There may be other explanations. Life, many argue, is incredibly resilient. Why?

- After life was created 3.8 billion years ago (or longer if panspermia occurred), it has continued to exist. Resilience of life is therefore self-evident.

- We know life likely formed once and has been in existence all these billions of years for several reasons based upon empirical data:

  » The same key molecules exist for all life, suggesting life has always existed no matter how primitive. It has not reinvented itself over and over. The same tRNA, stereoisomers, nucleic acids, and key molecular changes at the same sites of these key molecules with the same modification types exist for every living being.

» Fossils exist that demonstrate a continuous progression in the development of complex organisms. We see no history of complex, reasoning organisms anywhere before hominins, but a gradual development of complex species over a long period of time.

» Key changes in the atmosphere and geology match the types of organisms found on Earth at the time of those records. Our records of the history of the biosphere seem to match major catastrophic die-offs in the last 550 million years.

- Life's strength is dynamism, as its resilience is tested repeatedly over and over. We still continue to exist as we outflank nature. Life is winning against nature by evolving complexity, but is displacing natural hypodynamism with biologically-induced hyperdynamism. The hyperdynamism is becoming more complex, and the end result is a world with fragile hyperdynamic complexity that prevails against specific natural environments.

We must be careful, as life continues to exist for billions of years. But complex species change, and the changes are dramatic and even startling. While life is resilient, complex life is probably not. There is only one highly intelligent

**Human die-off**

A sudden killing off of individuals under the age of 40 (fertile members of society) because of an event. It could be one individual or it could be the entire human species who dies.

species today (*Homo sapiens*), and it has existed for only 4 million of the 4 billion years (one one-thousandth the time life has been on Earth), and complex civilization has existed only 10,000 years (less than 0.00025 percent of life's total existence) on Earth.

The Swiss-cheese view of our existence is an illusion. In a Swiss-cheese model life is highly highly highly unlikely. It is only unlikely simply because we have yet to fully understand the mechanisms, not because we magically appear from a godlike supernatural source. Yet, we formed because events turned into a planetary-formation world making life highly likely.

Similarly, the demise of life is highly likely if viewed as a planetary-formation model of interdependent event causation. It seems so unlikely through a Swiss-cheese prism and independent event causation. Because of the hyperdynamism and reflexivity existing within complex biological species, an illusion of stability exists when in fact our world is turning highly unstable.

## Transistor Problem-Solving Model

Given the amount of interconnectedness and the amount of unpredictability because of the exponential rise of complex biological organisms, we must make significant adjustments in our values and institutions to match this hyperdynamism. How?

- By acknowledging the emotion-laden world and the hyperdynamism that exists, we can confront our own self-annihilation more effectively. We have not understood this concept and even deny its existence.

- We are in a unique situation in our history to create massive feedback loops that are both positive and negative and that can cause wild swings in human behavior. We must focus on key solutions at key locations (like a transistor switch that can near-instantaneously turn on and off thousands to millions of other switches) that can dramatically impact all of us. This period is unique for four major reasons:

  » We are highly interconnected. Our ICQ is greater by a factor of $10^{10}$ and our ITQ by $10^7$ compared to a vast majority of our past as a species.

  » Our declining resources do not match the needs for our standard of living. We have gone from a near infinite resource Survivability Index (SI) to 268 in a matter of a thousand years.

  » The disparity in wealth has never been greater and never with such transparency. Some humans are living at or near the level of our primal past, suffering from chronic diseases and seeing with their own eyes the spectacle of others living in mansions with servants and in pristine health.

The Supercivilization: Essential Concepts

» The rise of technology dramatically empowers individuals to control all of human existence. Today, disadvantaged individuals can blackmail the world because of this interconnectedness and can achieve hopefulness in a hopeless world if they use nefarious means. They simply become desperate to change their world and will use technology to gain advantage where they see no hope.

- Conformity is a necessity for survival in highly interconnected civilizations. We can and should use emotion as a tool to create small solutions that resonate into huge solutions. However, it should be done with extreme caution and meticulous precision, as these transistor-like changes can turn pathological quite easily.

- Our only chance for survival is to create a sense of cohesion and brotherhood that is 100 percent inclusive and implement solutions through transistor problem-solving techniques.

- We would like a rational solution to our problems, but with the highly interconnected world, that is no longer possible. With too many complex beings possessing too many emotions, it is difficult to look for strictly rational solutions. Rational solutions are important, but effective emotional implementation is far more crucial.

- Independent will is no longer possible in our interconnected world. One person's freedom is another person's chains. Coordination and cooperation with rational solutions that promote cultural cohesion in an irrational way is our only hope for survival. We cannot survive in today's politically and culturally divided world of "us" versus "them".

## Classes of Events: Independent

Every risk analysis must include the classification of events that could lead to a significant die-off or self-annihilation. Given that events can occur independently and interdependently, I am classifying them based upon this relationship. Single independent events are divided into four types (Figure 5.1):

- **Class I Event:** This is defined as less than a 10 percent chance that a single event can lead to less than a 10 percent die-off of fertile members of society over a given 100 year period. This includes nearly all events of everyday life and living. These events number in the trillions everyday and make up an overwhelming majority of all events. They are inconsequential.

- **Class II Event:** This is defined as greater than a 10 percent chance that a single event can lead to less than a 10 percent die-off of fertile members of society over a given 100 year period. Human disease is a classic example.

- **Class III Event:** This is defined as less than a 10 percent chance that a single event can lead to greater than a 10 percent die-off of fertile members of society over a given 100 year period. A classic example is an asteroid impact.

- **Class IV Event:** This is defined as greater than a 10 percent chance that a single event can lead to greater than a 10 percent die-off of fertile members of society over a given 100 year period. We know of none today.

Single independent event etiologies are more a function of the natural world,

### Events

Any action, animate or inanimate in origin, that occurs which could lead to a die-off.

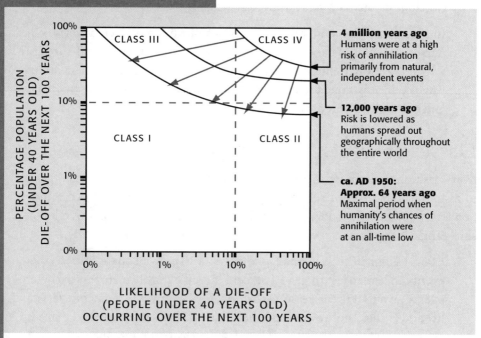

**FIGURE 5.1**  Humanity's Past: Primarily Singular Catastrophic Events (Author's Estimates Only)
*There is a possibility of a die-off (people under the age of forty) in any given one-hundred-year period in humanity's history because of natural, independent events. Humanity had little capability of determining our own future. No synergistic events of significance could occur because of low interconnectedness.*

The Supercivilization: Essential Concepts

its interaction, and its effect on us rather than the animate world. These events are mainly nonreflexive and we have virtually no hand in their development. These events are so rare that no Class IV Events that we know of exist today.

## Classes of Events: Interdependent

Now we describe interdependent events in which these events impact the chances that other events that are highly unlikely suddenly become more likely or even probable. Multiple interdependent events that affect other events in a chain reaction can have far more consequential effects on us (Figure 5.2):

- **Class V Event:** This is defined as less than a 10 percent chance that multiple events can lead to less than a 10 percent die-off of fertile members of society over a given 100 year period. Again this numbers in the trillions, but less than those in a Class I Event.

- **Class VI Event:** This is defined as greater than a 10 percent chance that multiple events can lead to less than a 10 percent die-off of fertile members of society over a given 100 year period. An example would be a series of diseases producing comorbid states in an individual.

- **Class VII Event:** This is defined as less than a 10 percent chance that multiple events can lead to greater than a 10 percent die-off of fertile members of society over a given 100 year period. A series of supervolcanic eruptions/earthquakes or series of asteroid impacts producing panic in a desperate Supercivilization is an example.

- **Class VIII Event:** This is defined as greater than 10 percent chance that multiple events can lead to greater than a 10 percent die-off of fertile members of society over a given 100 year period. This is a reality today. For example, multiple human-induced behavioral events like climate change and resource depletion leading to terrorism and then global thermonuclear war is a realistic possibility.

Class IV Events have always been a problem in our distant past, but because of our profound and effective ability to understand and control nature through the scientific method, Class IV Events no longer exist. We are lulled into complacency because of our successes against nature.

Class VIII Events never existed until modern humans existed, leading to profound and horrific ways we could annihilate ourselves through our interconnectedness. By 2040, I project humanity will be at its highest risk for a Class VIII Event in human history, but also at its greatest potential (because of our ability to create new technology) to decrease die-offs to their lowest threat level.

Today, we ignore a Class VIII Event because vested interests control the agenda. Utilizing resources to protect all of humanity against our own annihilation is discouraged by those with the most power, because under their own illusion of prosperity, they feel they will have to make the biggest sacrifice to save humanity. They don't realize a Class VIII Event potentially spares no one.

## The Essence of the Supercivilization: Discretionary Problem Solving

Because we are bound to a Supercivilization that has a common social contract requiring our unanimous signature, we are faced with an existence where free choice means defiance, opposition, and even violence. Discretionary problem solving now becomes our Achilles heel. Why?

- An abundance of choices in the hands of many leaders with unclear authority is a powerful concoction for disaster. We need strong leadership to guide humanity, not promote individual humans who have distinct material and resource advantages.

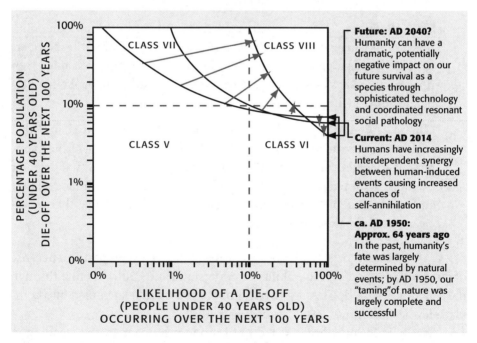

FIGURE 5.2    Humanity's Future: Primarily Synergistic, Multicausal Catastrophic Events (Author's Estimates Only)
*There is a possibility of a die-off (people under the age of forty) in any given one-hundred-year period in humanity's future because of interdependent, human-induced events acting synergistically to increase the chances of our annihilation. The amount of shift depends primarily on humans themselves—a unique development in our four-million-year history that is a result of high interconnectedness now and well into the future.*

The Supercivilization: Essential Concepts

- We now have an ability to solve problems that we know how to solve but no longer wish to solve. These types of problems are the hardest to deal with, but are a reality today. The problem-solving of today means solving problems for the greater good, not just for a small minority of individuals. We are forced to choose today.

- Solving problems is simply predicated on our desire to resolve them. Solutions now require unanimous consensus from all 7 billion people as typified by the climate change problem. Our final solutions will impact all 7 billion people in both positive and negative ways simply from the potential solutions we do not wish to select. Self-sacrifice is mandatory and not a luxury or even a discretionary question any longer.

- Medicine and its steady increase in resource utilization typifies the Supercivilization. Do we expend almost endless resources for diminishing returns of success on people who have little value to society? Are we doing a service or disservice to everyone who needs the ultimate medical therapy, regardless of expense? Where do we draw the line? Who decides? These answers are problematic—and the essence of the Supercivilization (Figure 5.3).

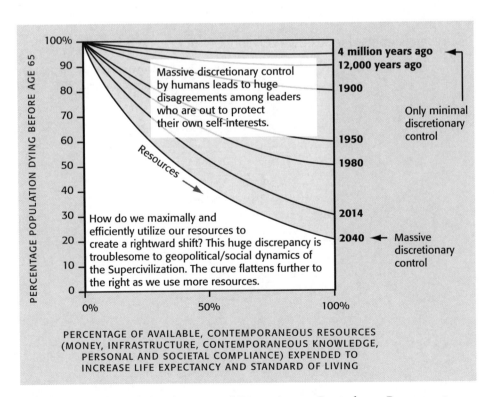

FIGURE 5.3  The Supercivilization and Discretionary Control over Resources to Improve Life Expectancy and Standard of Living (Conceptual Only)

Chapter 6

# Purely Natural Problems

"Everyone is entitled to his own opinion, but not his own facts."

*—Daniel Patrick Moynihan, US ambassador*
*to the United Nations, 1975–1976*

# Definitions of Events and Problems

For the next four chapters, I classify events or problems into the following two major categories.

- Nature-induced events or problems: This is any event or problem that occurs without human activity. It may occur because of inanimate or animate causes, but not because of humans.

- Human-induced events or problems: This is any event or problem that occurs incidentally, accidentally, or purposefully, and is caused by humans.

Some events are purely nature-induced, some primarily nature-induced, some primarily human-induced, and others purely human-induced.

## Purely Natural Events with a Greater-Than-One-in-One-Hundred-Thousand Chance of Occurring

In this chapter, I look strictly at nature-induced events or problems that stand a reasonable chance of triggering a human-induced die-off of significance (greater than a one-percent die-off of the human species over a one-hundred-year period). Because currently no such events can be seen on the horizon that could cause this type of die-off, I focus on three major types of natural events that have roughly a one-in-one-hundred-thousand chance or greater of occurring in the next hundred years. Purely natural events of major consequence for humanity are exceedingly rare. They are so exceedingly rare that our focus on preventing these types of events is probably misplaced.

Three major types of purely natural events could occur over the next one-hundred years:

- Supernova explosion

- Supervolcano explosion

- Asteroid impact

All three types have the following characteristics in common:

- They all will be quite obvious when they occur. The nonscientist can understand these problems, because the events are well-defined and discrete. Scientists can explain their occurrences quite easily.

- The events will occur quickly and definitively. No scientists will have to explain to the general population when these problems happen. These events will occur over a matter of a few days to weeks and will not languish with uncertainty for years or centuries.

- Few vested interests will benefit from delay. These are problems that require additional actions and do not require withdrawing activities; goods or services are already in place. These events are so overwhelmingly horrific that even those interests that must allocate resources can see these events coming and the universal destruction that will result will be massive and unforgiving.

- These events can be forecast well before they occur. We can plan for their occurrence accurately, because causation is mathematically predictable.

- These events or problems will not be subject to the Moser biological uncertainty principle. When we study these events, we have little effect on them. We can affect their occurrence but only volitionally and in a purely inhibitory, not inductive, fashion.

- Most important, one of those catastrophic events are probably not going to occur anyway in the next hundred years. Those events are all in the one-in-a-thousand to tens-of-thousands chance to occur at best. In the last 600 million years (Figure 6.1 A to C) there have been six notable die-offs of the biosphere; all were related to those catastrophic events or some variant or combination of those events.

## Supernova Explosion or Gamma-Ray Burst

When a star dies, it collapses on itself. This collapse can either be a slow collapse over hundreds to millions to billions of years (like our sun will experience as a black dwarf with little energy release) or one gigantic collapse with a sudden jolt lasting days to even minutes (Figure 6.2). A large, sudden collapse occurs with a large star that will offer tremendous bursts of energy (gamma rays) that will radiate intense and lethal particles that will kill anyone or anything near it. The causes and consequences are as follows:

- An end-of-life explosion of a star that is at least ten times as large as our sun will cause a supernova explosion. These types of stars, although a small percentage of stars in the universe, can create numerous threats to its surrounding planetary neighbors extending thousands of light years away. The two major types of gamma-ray bursts are as follows:

  » **Supernova:** This produces debris of high-energy particles and gamma rays that spread out throughout a 360-degree field. This would be deadly for all life on Earth if present less than 25 light years away.

  » **Hypernova:** This is even larger and it produces debris concentrated over two linear directions because of magnetic field effects. With the

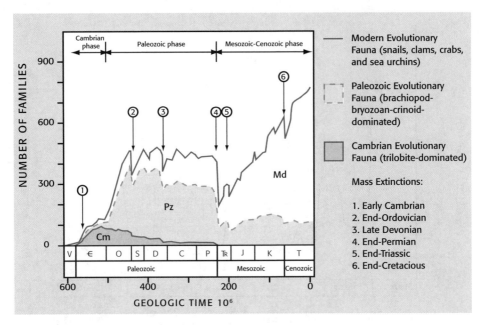

**FIGURE 6.1 A** Marine Diversity with the Six Major Phanerozoic Extinctions (Past 600 Million Years)

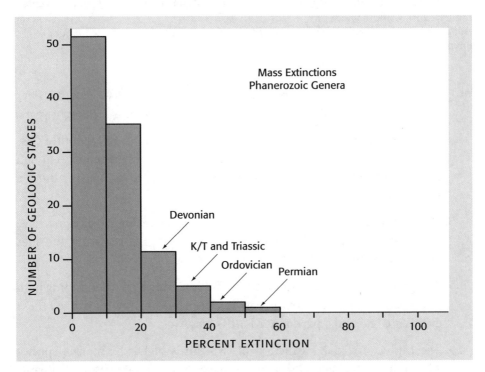

**FIGURE 6.1 B** Intensity of Extinctions During the Phanerozoic (Last 542 Million Years)
*This figure shows that significant extinctions occur quite frequently and involve more than half of the geologic stages of the phanerozoic. Extinctions are common and a continuum, not distinct and rare.*

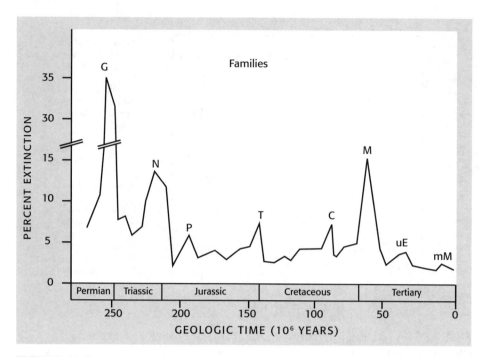

**FIGURE 6.1 C**  Regular and Periodic Extinctions of Marine Family Diversity over the Past 250 Million Years
*Apparently every 26 million years an extinction occurs above baseline. Extinctions are a regular occurrence.*

debris/gamma ray field concentrated so intensely in just two directions, these could kill all living organisms on Earth if within 7500 light years.

- No known stars near us are predicted to explode in the near future (less than a million years from now), but calculations are not refined enough to guarantee this. This uncertainty is what makes a gamma-ray burst a possible event.

- At least three large gamma-ray bursts causing major extinctions have occurred since Earth formed 4.6 billion years ago. These are only the ones we can confirm. It is likely there were more.

- A supernova most likely occurred 2.8 million years ago. After finding high $^{60}$Fe levels at the bottom of the Pacific Ocean, we are now convinced these events are real and a part of our Earth's history.

- The End-Ordovician extinction of two-thirds of Earth's marine species 440 million years ago is thought to have occurred as a result of a gamma-ray burst.

- Prevention is a fait acompli. Nothing can be done if we discover a nearby supernova. We have no defense, which makes this event unworthy of

The Supercivilization: Essential Concepts

study. To devote further resources to prevent this event would be a waste of resources.

## Massive Asteroid Impact

Asteroids have played a significant role in the history of Earth (Figure 6.3). It is only recently that we have discovered how significant they have been. Asteroid impacts are common, they are real, and they are potentially catastrophic for humanity.

- Asteroids are loosely defined as an object in space measuring between ten meters wide and the size of a minor planet (size of Pluto). They are made of rock which can vary in density from iron to styrofoam depending upon their makeup.

| Spectral Type | Approximate Percentage of Stars in This Class | Surface Temperature (°C) | Luminosity (solar units) | Mass (solar units) | Lifetime (years) | End of Star's Life | |
|---|---|---|---|---|---|---|---|
| | | | | | | Type of Death | Amt of Energy Release over Time |
| O | 0.001% | 50,000 | 1,000,000 | 60 | 500 thousand | Supernova, then black hole (largest) or neutron star (smallest) | Massive, quick release of energy |
| B | 0.1% | 15,000 | 1,000 | 6 | 50 million | Neutron star/ white dwarf | Potentially large and quick release of energy or smaller with fading release |
| A | 1% | 8,000 | 20 | 2 | 1 billion | White dwarf | Moderate with fading release |
| F | 2% | 6,500 | 7 | 1.5 | 2 billion | White dwarf | Mild with slowly fading release |
| G | 7% | 5,500 | 1 | 1 | 10 billion | White dwarf | Very mild with very slowly fading release |
| K | 15% | 4,000 | 0.3 | 0.7 | 20 billion | White dwarf | Minimal with extremely slowly fading release |
| L | 75% | 3,000 | 0.003 | 0.2 | 600 billion | White dwarf | Extremely minimal with barely emitting energy at infinitesimally long release |

FIGURE 6.2 Typical Properties for Hydrogen-Burning Stars of the Seven Major Spectral Types
*Sun is a G type. The bigger the stars are, the shorter their life spans, the more quickly their resources are used, the fewer the numbers of stars, and the more violent their endings. Is this a model for human civilizations?*

- Asteroid impacts with Earth are likely to occur in our generation. The last major impact was Tunguska in 1908 that was 10 to 20 meters wide and leveled millions of trees in Russia.

- The last major asteroid to kill off a sizeable portion of the biosphere was just 65 million years ago when the dinosaurs were killed by an explosion of a 10 kilometer-wide asteroid that landed in the Gulf of Mexico.

- Asteroid impacts are the easiest to fight of the three major natural problems for several reasons:

  » We know how to change the path of an asteroid should it travel in the Earth's path. We now have the technology to prevent an asteroid collision.

  » The average person can easily understand this concept, as small asteroid (meteors under a meter) collisions happen all the time. Twenty to forty tons of material impact the Earth's atmosphere every day.

  » Potentially dangerous asteroids can be seen years before they impact us. They are not mysterious; to take away any uncertainty, their courses can be calculated reliably by astronomers.

  » The potential solution is relatively cheap compared to other problems. It is estimated an asteroid rendezvous would cost humanity $10 to 20 billion which is a mere fraction (less than 0.1 percent) of the gross world product.

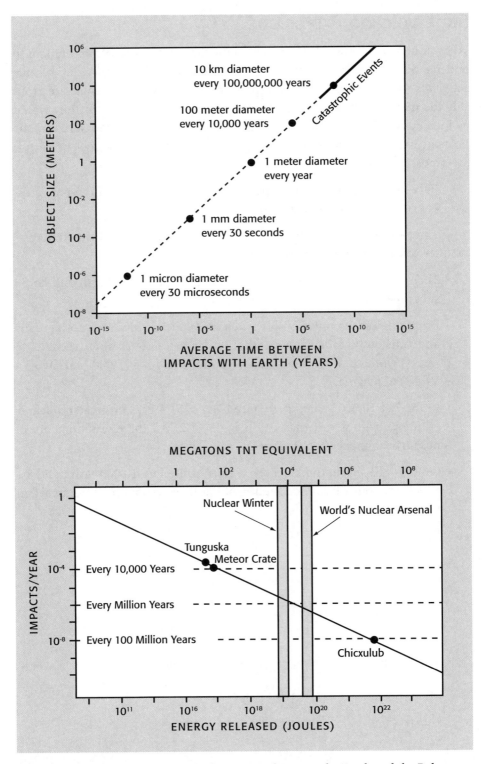

**FIGURE 6.3** Relative Likelihood of an Asteroid Hitting the Earth and the Relative Damage That Would Be Produced

# Supervolcano Explosions

Volcanic activity is probably the easiest of the three natural events for humans to understand, as these events are occurring around us all the time. While volcanic activity is common, supervolcano explosions are relatively rare. These are probably the most problematic of the three types of natural events, as they would be incredibly difficult to stop. The size of volcanic activity is measured by the Volcanic Explosivity Index, which is logarithmic in scale from 1 (least powerful) to 8 (most powerful).

- Fifty to 60 eruptions on land per year occur with a larger unknown number coming from undersea activity.

- Three to 5 times as much material is estimated to emanate from underwater volcanic activity as from land activity.

- There are 550 known active volcanoes throughout the Earth and 45-50 supervolcanoes.

- Eruptions can be mild (VEI-1) such as Kilauea, which is erupting daily and constantly, to a massive eruption lasting a short time (seconds to weeks) while spewing more than 1000 km$^3$ (Mt Toba 73,000 years ago—a VEI-8) of magma.

- In the last 10,000 years, there have been 4751 VEI-2 or greater volcanic eruptions with a vast majority being VEI-2. All these eruptions are of near-trivial impact to humanity.

- Only 5 VEI-7 eruptions occurred during the last 10,000 years and no VEI-8 eruptions have occurred, making these eruptions infrequent but not nonexistent.

# Supervolcano Frequency and Odds

While rare, these supervolcano explosions can cause climate changes for the entire Earth, leading to sunlight inhibition and the destruction of the biosphere. These supervolcanoes are real and extremely dangerous. Our huge advantage is that we understand geology enough to predict when these events can and will occur. We are likely to know years, perhaps decades, before a supervolcano will explode and how these events will unfold. The main advantage today is there are no supervolcanoes, that we know of, that are anywhere near close to erupting. In summary the odds are as follows:

- There have been 42 documentable VEI-8 (types that would threaten the entire biosphere) supervolcanoes in the past 36 million years (they erupt once every 850,000 years on average).

- Two VEI-8 explosions have occurred in the past 100,000 years (once every 50,000 years on average) with one 74,000 years ago and the last one 26,000 years ago.

- There is a 0.2 percent chance, using this information alone, that a VEI-7 eruption could occur in the next hundred years.

- Formal estimates by vulcanologists put the odds at a 1 percent chance of a VEI-8 occurring between 460 to 7,200 years from now. Between now and 460 years from now the odds are much much lower than that.

- Little could be done to protect against this event, and given these odds, few resources should be used to protect against a VEI-8 supervolcanic explosion.

Chapter 7

# Primarily Natural Problems

"Medicare and Medicaid account for 22.9 percent of all federal spending today. By 2017 these programs will consume nearly 33 percent of all federal spending. Unless we make some drastic changes, by 2050 Medicare and Medicaid will consume more than all federal taxes. By 2080 Medicare alone will consume all federal taxes."

*—Ezekiel Emanuel, MD,*
*PhD, noted health care reformer*

# Treatment Disparities Between First and Third World

Today, the real issue with resolving disease isn't whether we have the capability; it is whether we have the *will*. Merely finding an answer to the scientific question posed is not enough. Social factors become the key variable for problem-solving as demonstrated by these startling statistics of the 21st century:

- **Tetanus:** Five people died in the United States in 2001 from tetanus. In some parts of Africa, 10 to 30 percent of all children die of this disease, which means hundreds of thousands of children are dying needlessly from a fully preventable disease. A tetanus vaccination is all that is needed to prevent this disease.

- **Tuberculosis:** Tuberculosis killed 764 people in the United States in 2001, but in the rest of the world, 1.6 million died of TB that same year. Three out of 1,000,000 people die annually from TB in the United States, but 238 people out of 1,000,000 die annually worldwide. Two billion people carry TB in its dormant state, yet only 14,000 people in the United States (or 0.0045 percent) have the active form. Isolation and antibiotics are usually 100 percent effective.

- **Syphilis:** Thirty-six people in the United States in 2001 died from syphilis, but worldwide, syphilis killed 156,000 people that same year. Syphilis is easily identified with a blood test and can be treated with penicillin successfully 100 percent of the time.

- **Whooping cough:** Pertussis (whooping cough) killed 17 people in the United States in 2001, yet in the rest of world 301,000 children died that same year. A vaccine is nearly 100 percent effective. Children who are infected can easily be identified, isolated, and treated with a penicillin derivative and cured 100 percent of the time.

# Nature of Disease: Primarily a Natural Problem with Social Components

Unlike purely natural problems, disease has social components in its development and treatment that complicate its eradication. Some facts about disease are as follows:

- Theoretical solutions are often found, but implementation of those solutions is far more difficult than purely natural problems.

- Disease is not discrete, but continuous, making it a far more difficult problem to resolve. How is disease defined? It is unclear what disease is.

- Purely natural problems (such as earthquakes, tornadoes, other natural disasters) killed an average of 62,000 people in the world annually in the 1990s, as compared to communicable diseases, which killed millions.

- If we are having so much difficulty treating the four diseases above, which are easy to spot, easy to isolate, and easy to treat, what chance do we have against more serious diseases of far more complexity?

## Today's Diseases of the First World

The diseases of the 21st century now take on fundamental differences from those in the past. Diseases become chronic in nature, and the acute diseases that killed off individuals pre-21st century quickly are becoming less prevalent. Twenty-first century diseases have the following characteristics in common:

- They usually affect individuals older than fifty, making for a multitude of risk factors and behavioral issues that cloud their etiologies.

- They are not discrete. Those who have them are not easily identified until it is too late and therefore difficult to identify before they cause major, irreversible pathology.

- They are often misunderstood (for example, the exact cause of atherosclerosis), leading to a great deal of confusion, wasted efforts, and resources spent on questionable treatments.

- They have complex multifactorial mechanisms (a multitude of pathways leading to complex interactions between intrinsic mechanisms of the body).

- Treatments for these diseases are frequently ineffective, partial, or of limited benefit. They are also exponentially more expensive to treat, given the necessary scientific advancements.

- Age is a risk factor for these processes, and therefore no one is ever cured. Individuals merely fend off the disease until a future time at which they eventually succumb to that illness.

Three major diseases—heart disease, stroke, and cancer—now make up a majority of humanity's deaths. They kill more than two out of three people in the First World. They epitomize the problem of fighting chronic disease today.

# Some Major Problems in Curing Disease

As we become better at fighting diseases that are the low-hanging fruit (such as the monofactorial diseases caused by infectious organisms), we create long-term chronic illnesses which produce permanent comorbidities in individuals. These individuals now serve as a nidus for further illnesses that are even more difficult to fight. The following is a result:

- We discover disease will never go away. People will always have disease, simply based upon its spurious definition.

- Much disease stems from the complex interplay between humans and other organisms. We cannot exist without other organisms. We are heterotrophs so we need the biosphere to survive, yet it is at the heart of most disease processes (even the noninfectious diseases occur in part as a result of our immune system—designed to protect us from invaders—causing unwanted side effects, such as atherosclerosis, in defending us). It is a losing battle to ever think that disease, especially infectious diseases, can be eliminated forever and completely.

- As we beat the biosphere and other organisms at natural selection, we make it harder on ourselves to survive. The elimination of the biosphere changes our environment and creates new unseen challenges as well as organisms more resistant to our solutions. Other microscopic organisms become our primary challenge, not the macroscopic organisms we have dominated for centuries.

- The more cures we create for people from insults, the more comorbidities we create in humans as they get older. This alone makes more humans more susceptible to disease, and the spread of infectious disease becomes facilitated.

- Resources to resolve disease are expended mainly as we get older and accumulate more insults. Resources become vastly more expensive to treat individuals as we get older.

- All countries who have successfully extended life spans of their citizens have seen major rises in health care costs in the 21st century. The United States leads with 17.3 percent of its GDP spent on health care.

- Health care is expensive not because we are wasteful (as most people believe); it is because we are so *successful in our treatments of sick individuals.*

- To promote their products, vested interests promote the illusion of need in individuals who are not necessarily unhealthy.

- The medical-industrial complex is so byzantine and divorced from the patient (a product of the sociologically modern human) that it forgets its main overarching purpose—cure humans of illness and not necessarily generate profits.

## Western Diseases: We are Acquiring More Diseases But They are Less Severe and More Subjective

In the First World, diseases are more prevalent than ever, yet objectively we have never been healthier. Why?

- The number of diseases is growing, but the severity is lessening. Restless leg syndrome and depression are replacing tuberculosis and smallpox as diseases in the First World.

- Most new diseases have to do with mind-body interactions and less with objective findings. We worry about trivial diseases that in the past were irrelevant. With the elimination of truly dangerous diseases comes the obsession with disease—any disease.

- Obsessive compulsive disorder—a highly speculative, subjective, and controversial diagnosis—was recently determined to be the most prevalent psychiatric disorder in the United States.

- Fibromyalgia is even a questionable disease (connective tissues, such as muscles throughout the entire body that appear to have intermittent and debilitating pain) that is still misunderstood. It has an unknown cause, is highly subjective, and is even dismissed by many doctors as nothing more than depression.

- Pressure is placed on doctors by the medical-industrial complex to placate patients and diagnose conditions, even if they are phantom. There is immediate backlash from patients, families, support groups, and the pharmaceutical industry for any doctor to suggest any subjective-based disease is not "real." Physician-patient relationships are not isolated from the reimbursement process, because most doctors receive reimbursements mainly from government entities, which are manipulated by the medical-industrial complex.

- No physician can say with certainty that individuals are disease free. Virtually all patients leave any office or clinic today with a diagnosis, any diagnosis. Doctors cannot say if these diseases are truly physiologically-based, since disease no longer requires a physiological or anatomical basis for its definition. It merely requires a functional definition.

# Inverted and Opposing Growth Curves of Efficacy and Resource Expenditure

As we get to the 20th century and the sociologically modern human (Figure 7.1), we see two curves inflecting in the opposite directions (Figures 7.2 A to C). As medical costs rise exponentially (convex curve), the efficacy of those treatments (concave curve) are declining to the point of a steady state as far as objective benefits.

- In the first part of the 20th century, efficacy in treatments rose far faster than expenditures.

- By the end of the 20th century, efficacy in treatments rose far slower than expenditures.

- As we continue to "conquer" disease, we expend more money per treatment.

- However, our treatments are far less consequential; if we compare two countries with similar objective health care indicator success (Cuba and United States), we see huge differences in costs per capita annually ($186/person in Cuba compared to $4500/person in the United States).

- The more money we spend on our health care, the more flattening of this success curve. It is inevitable and seemingly beyond our control. As long as there is a free market and no one to objectively

## Illusion of need

Because of our mandatory socialization during the modern period, we buy things not because we need them but because we believe we need them. We buy things because other people are buying them. Without these products we feel unfulfilled and nonsocial. Prior to the development of the sociological being, there was less control over our psyche than there is today, especially by others, who provide goods and services. Because of our inability to escape the Supercivilization and its profound interconnectedness, we are convinced by vested interests that we need their products; we no longer merely desire their products.

constrain these vested interests, these diverging curves will continue their expansion.

## Continuous Nature of Disease

As our abilities to fight disease improve, we become impeded by our own inability to distinguish the disease state from the non-disease state. Our abilities to scrutinize those with disease become highly compromised. Our classification of disease as to its functional nature made little impact on our success. Today that has changed. Why?

- Before the 20th century, disease was seen as black and white simply because the battles we were fighting were so overwhelming that little understanding of minor illnesses was relatively inconsequential.

- Death was the endpoint in most cases preceded by suffering from disease. All other diseases were trivial and required relatively little attention.

- Because so little was known about disease, the few theories we had remained unchallenged.

- Roy Porter, noted medical historian comments, "Before the Victorian era, medicine had but paltry power to cure disease and save the sick, and few entertained great expectations of it."

- Discoveries in the 20th century outstrip our theories. Our knowledge about ourselves is too great to be explained by existing theories so we often seek functional rather than etiological categories for disease.

## Problematic Nature of the Definition of Disease

While we would like to have a definitive definition of the disease state, we do not have one. There will never be a satisfactory definition. Why?

- Disease has always been and will always be a functional classification and not etiological, because we will never know the true cause of all diseases. Why? If we do not have a satisfactory definition for life itself (prion versus virus versus bacteria versus human), how can we confidently assume that a definition of an abnormal state of a living organism also would be straightforward?

- The online definition of disease from dictionary.com is even more nebulous: "[A] disordered or incorrectly functioning organ, part, structure, or system of the body resulting from genetic, developmental errors, infection, poisons, nutritional deficiency or imbalance, toxicity, or unfavorable environmental factors." One can make a case that all seven billion humans could be seriously diseased with this definition at this very moment.

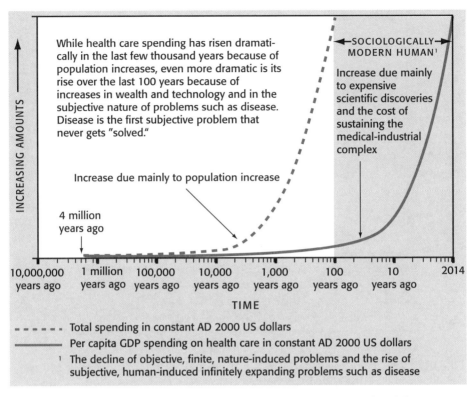

**FIGURE 7.1** Health Care Spending in Human History (Conceptual Only) *This figure shows per capita GDP spending on health care and total health care spending vs. time.*

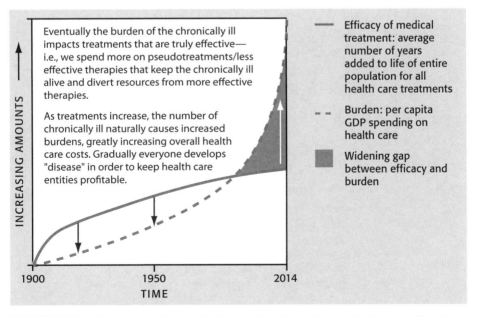

**FIGURE 7.2 A** Natural Problem with Health Care Spending in the Supercivilization of the Past 114 Years (Conceptual Only)

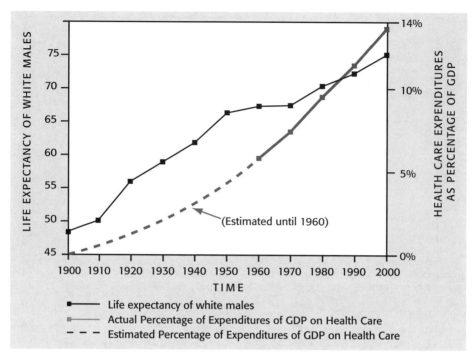

FIGURE 7.2 B   Life Expectancy of White Males and Health Care Expenditures as Percentage of GDP vs. Time in the United States

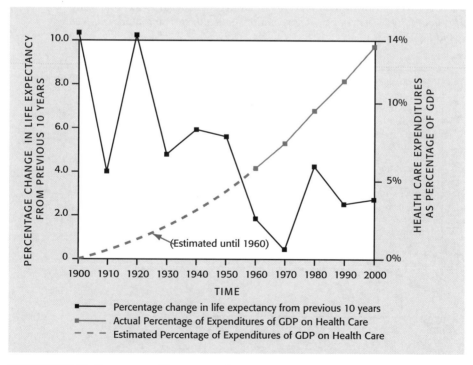

FIGURE 7.2 C   Percentage Change in Life Expectancy over the Previous 10 Years and Health Care Expenditures as Percentage of GDP vs. Time in the United States

- Since pathology is a relative term, it will never disappear. Never. Pathology means abnormal functioning of an organism relative to a "healthy norm." What is a healthy norm? It is relative and not absolute. If the normal distribution curve has two tails, then pathology is an artificial line drawn in the sand. Who determines where these tails are "normal" and "abnormal?" We ourselves do, which is entirely subjective.

## Multifactorial Nature of Disease as We Age

Our bodies are genetically programmed to live a specified period of time. Once we have maximized our chances to live past the fertile years and approach senescence, our diseases become multifactorial in nature and are exponentially more difficult to cure:

- Evolutionarily, as we age, more complex mechanisms break down at more locations causing synergistic pathology.

- After reproductive age we take on vastly more complex disease etiologies that require exponentially more resources to fight. Success can be attained, but only at a cost. Does it become worthwhile to "fix" an older organism? That question is easy for the child, but what about the 96 year old?

- Two major types of disease of aging people—atherosclerosis and cancer—involve multifactorial, unclear, and intrinsic processes. There is no definitive beginning or ending to these two disease processes. See pages 119 to 120 for more information.

## Fighting Disease Today: Burden Versus Lethality

Prior to the sociologically modern human, success against disease was measured via a single axis: the treatment and elimination of that disease. In the era of the sociologically modern human, disease now has two axes: its burden and its lethality. Our potential to treat individuals at any and/or all cost becomes extremely problematic.

- Heavy-burden diseases are worse for society; highly lethal diseases are worse for the individual succumbing to that disease. Highly lethal diseases kill people quickly, which facilitates societal protection.

- Most lethal diseases of the youngest people (smallpox, Ebola, plague, cholera) are the easiest to fight because patient cooperation is not a problem. The patient is fully compliant because of the following:

  » These diseases are dramatically painful.

  » They are highly infectious.

- » The incubation period is swift causing symptoms almost immediately.

- » The patient is too weak to resist treatment, eliminating the spread as a result of denial/noncompliance.

- » Isolation of victims is extremely easy given their early declaration of symptoms and the severity of their illness.

- Most lethal diseases are monofactorial, which makes patients easy to treat without the need for human cooperation.

- Heavy-burden diseases require huge resources for a huge number of victims; we are collecting these at an extraordinary clip:

  - » **Common cold:** This costs $40 billion in direct and indirect costs annually to the United States. It is in some ways the most dangerous organism. Because it is so benign, we mainly ignore our symptoms and spread the disease.

  - » **Influenza:** With this disease, the host is more ill so this disease is slightly more difficult to spread because of the lethargy of the individual, which produces self-induced isolation. Still it is spread often before individuals are aware of their infection (or work through their infection) and the relatively rare death makes it more likely to expend more resources to fight it.

- The highest-burden diseases now require far more cooperation of all individuals than at any other time in the history of humanity. They have now surpassed the most lethal diseases as our greater threat.

Heavy burden diseases are taking over the Supercivilization. Because of the sociological nature of our biosociophysical environment today, we are fighting a losing battle, resulting in diminished problem-solving capabilities and disastrous consequences.

## Six Major Disease Processes Indicative of the Sociologically Modern Human's Fight for Survival

Because diseases no longer kill off individuals to the extent they did prior to the 20th century, we see high-burden diseases as our major problem. Today, six diseases—malaria, tuberculosis, HIV, atherosclerosis, cancer, and diabetes—are the most problematic because of their heavy and growing burden. They serve as an unfortunate reminder to all of us: our need to fight disease not merely demands solutions, but *requires* the most efficient and effective solutions. Currently, "solutions" to these diseases tend to benefit the medical-industrial complex far more than the patient. Some generalizations can be made about these six diseases:

- They make up a majority of the most deadly disease processes we see today.

- The first three diseases—malaria, tuberculosis, and HIV—are communicable diseases striking the Third World in the greatest numbers. They are problematic because treatments require complete cooperation of the individual and a well-integrated medical system that can deliver treatments efficiently and effectively. Resources are limited for both their prevention and treatment.

- The last three diseases—atherosclerosis, cancer, and diabetes—are a result of the aging process. They involve disease processes that occur simply because society has too much success and too many resources used in treating lethal diseases earlier in life. These three diseases are not a problem until we successfully eliminate monofactorial-caused diseases of the young.

## Malaria

Malaria remains a major threat for the following reasons:

- This disease kills nearly a million people per year. Individuals who die reside mainly in the Third World and often do not receive adequate treatment.

## Malaria

An infectious disease endemic to the tropics. It causes cyclical fevers, profound weakness, and in many it causes death. It is caused by a protozoa introduced through a mosquito bite that invades and destroys red blood cells in humans.

- The *Plasmodium falciparum* protozoa produces a carrier state that causes cyclical fevers, which is most devastating mainly to the old and young.

- Those most virile victims are incapacitated, but serve as an effective breeding ground for transmission by other mosquitoes.

- People linger as carriers for weeks to months to years, serving as breeding grounds for others to become infected.

- Most virile individuals cannot perform at their most efficient levels, so infrastructure languishes in endemic areas. Poor economic productivity leads to infrastructure depletion and more susceptibility to mosquito vectors.

- Humoral and cellular immunity is never achieved because of the nature of the organism (a protozoa), and therefore patients can easily be reinfected. Vaccinations are difficult because of this same problem.

- Disease is a three-vector problem (mosquito, human, and the protozoa itself), making eradication extremely difficult and expensive. All three vectors need to be eliminated simultaneously before total success can be achieved.

## Tuberculosis

Tuberculosis is caused by *Mycobactrium tuberculosis*—a slow-growing airborne bacteria residing in the lungs. Tuberculosis remains a major threat for the following reasons:

- Tuberculosis is highly infectious. The *Mycobacterium tuberculosis* is located in the sputum secretions of anyone infected, making its spread effective.

- Tuberculosis kills roughly a million people every year— mainly in the Third World.

- Individuals are often unaware they have the disease. If untreated, slow death occurs.

- Individuals suspected of harboring tuberculosis need to see a doctor to have a PPD placed. They need to have it read in exactly 72 hours to determine if it is positive.

- Treatment requires taking medication daily over a course of several months, which is extremely difficult to adhere to for those most likely to be infected.

- Individuals who have this illness in the First World usually have substance abuse issues, are often homeless, and are usually without resources.

- Individuals must meticulously isolate themselves for several months until their infectivity is eliminated. This is extremely difficult for individuals without resources.

- Many times, after patients are treated initially, they stop taking their medications because they feel better. The *Mycobacterium* eventually returns, only to be resistant to the antibiotics because of the abbreviated treatment. Treatments are gradually becoming ineffective.

## HIV

Human immunodeficiency virus (HIV) is a slow-replication retrovirus that causes the acquired immunodeficiency syndrome (AIDS). HIV exploded in the last two decades of the 20th century after it went unrecognized for several years. HIV existed for perhaps hundreds of thousands of years in the primate population and somehow transferred its infectivity to the human population.

HIV/AIDS is a major threat for the following reasons:

- Millions are currently infected in the human population. Roughly a million people die every year from HIV infection.

- The single advantage HIV has, compared to tuberculosis and malaria, is that it is more difficult to transmit (only after direct contact mainly with blood and/or semen).

- Currently, HIV can kill carriers over months to years without treatment. But with treatment, we can extend someone's life span by decades. It can become a mild chronic disease process. We can significantly reduce transmissibility with adequate treatment.

- Patients are required to monitor for side effects from daily medications they will take for the rest of their lives and for the progression of their illness. Both of these tasks are expensive and time consuming.

- Those who have the disease may not realize they have it.

- HIV flourishes in the areas on Earth with few resources, thereby making its complete eradication extremely difficult.

## Atherosclerosis

Atherosclerosis is the hardening and narrowing of the arteries because of plaque formation, resulting in a sudden plaque rupture, leading to heart attack or stroke. The development of coronary artery and cerebrovascular disease as a side effect of our immune system's defenses against invaders is near universal, but its progression varies between individuals, families, and cultures. Thousands of steps are involved in the biochemical pathways leading to this disease. Atherosclerosis has no clear beginning, but usually starts in childhood.

The cofactors leading to atherosclerosis are numerous and do not necessarily cause atherosclerosis, but merely put us at risk. Causes can be, for example, environmental exposures (salt in diet), physiological dysfunction (hypertension, hyperlipidemia, genetics, diabetes), behavioral issues (decreased exercise, diet, smoking), and many other biological cofactors and pathways. It is extremely difficult to fight because it contains so many variables (sociological, biological and physical) that lead to its causation, and the process is poorly understood. Atherosclerosis will continue to be a major problem in our lives for the following reasons:

- In the 21st century, it plays a role in the death of well over half the human population. It is the major cause of serious pathology in the aging members of the Supercivilization. As more members age, more people develop atherosclerosis.

- Lightning quick pathologies (sudden cardiac death, stroke) can strike at anytime without warning. These can be irreversibly fatal and make this disease process extremely insidious and destructive before we even know we have the disease.

- Fatal, irreversible disease processes usually occur at the end of this process, not its beginning when treatments are more effective.

- We have no quick, easy, noninvasive, and accurate tests for atherosclerosis. Each test that is more accurate in its diagnosis, is progressively more invasive and dangerous for the patient. Cardiac catheterization is the gold standard to determine coronary artery disease—a subcategory of this disease that is perhaps the most lethal. A mortality rate from this procedure is 0.1 percent, and a major complication rate of 2 percent currently exists. Costs for the procedure are in the thousands of dollars, making this test impractical for unselected use.

- Treatments are often ineffective, especially at its latest stages. Even elective stenting has been called into question, leaving mortality rates with little or no change.

- Behavior modification is the best known treatment. This requires cultural change as well as individual change. Given the age of the individual and the learned behaviors that are difficult to change throughout one's lifetime, this becomes an extremely challenging disease to fight.

- Intervention with one etiology is rarely productive, as multiple interventions—at great cost—are necessary to achieve significant success.

The Supercivilization: Essential Concepts

## Cancer

Cancer is uncontrolled, abnormal cell growth, with the potential to invade or spread to other parts of the body. The cause of the transformation is diverse and unique to different cancer types. The type of cancer depends on the cell type that undergoes this change. Ultimate consequences vary according to cell type, individual, family, and types of environmental exposures.

Like atherosclerosis, cancer's onset is unclear. Unlike atherosclerosis, cancer is a compilation of multiple types of pathology with some causes that are clear and others that are a complete mystery to doctors. Many variables (sociological, biological, and physical) lead to its causation. In general, cancer is caused by several types of insults, such as microorganisms, toxins, environmental factors, and genetic errors.

Determining when the pathology begins can be difficult, as there is no definitive beginning. It could start at conception, at birth, early in life, after the first insult or subsequent insults, with immune response problems, or even when there is conscious recognition of the problem.

Cancer will continue to be a major problem in our lives for the following reasons:

- At some point cancer will be diagnosed in well over half and kill roughly a third of all humans alive today.

- The complexities of cancer are mind-boggling and confusing even to doctors. Identification of its existence is sometimes extremely difficult. Some screening tests, such as PSA and digital rectal exams (for prostate cancer), mammograms (for breast cancer), and colonoscopies (for colorectal cancer), to name a few, while uncomfortable, are necessary.

- Cancer requires multiple modes of therapies, multiple treatments, and multiple follow up visits. Treatments such as surgery and chemotherapy are painful and expensive; some are inordinately unknown.

- Intervention (surgery, chemotherapy, radiation therapy, bone marrow transplants, etc) by preventing one single etiology is nearly impossible for achieving significant success.

- Rarely is anyone ever cured without a caveat that the cancer could return, leaving the patient and the family with tremendous uncertainty.

## Diabetes

Diabetes is the quintessential disease of modern humans and the Supercivilization, as it is directly related to modern lifestyles that promote inactivity and encourage the consumption of a great deal of food. Most likely, as the world's population ages, costs will continue to rise in the Supercivilization for treatments in a never-ending attempt to stave off this disease.

There are two types of diabetes:

- **Type I:** This is impaired production of insulin from the pancreas because of autoimmune factors.

- **Type II (90 percent of all diabetics):** This is either impaired resistance to insulin by end organs, decreased insulin production from the pancreas, or a combination of both. Roughly two-thirds of Type II diabetes is a result of obesity.

The metabolic syndrome (associated with atherosclerosis) is directly related to Type II hyperinsulinemic individuals (roughly half of all diabetics). Diabetes will continue to be a major problem in our lives for the following reasons:

- Thirty-five percent of people over 60 and 26 percent of people over 25 have impaired fasting glucose (pre-diabetes) or diabetes. Twenty-three percent of people over 60 have diabetes and 11 percent over age 25 have it.

- Rising diabetes rates are directly related to obesity (80 percent of diabetics are obese). There are currently 23.6 million diabetics in the United States alone.

- All diabetics have double the risk of dying at all ages because of their illness.

- The effects of diabetes can be managed (and occasionally reversed) through a multitude of interventions, including dietary and daily monitoring regimens which can be very burdensome and *require voluntary compliance and mandatory cooperation by the patient*. Patients must spend hundreds, sometimes even thousands, of hours a year on various tasks like losing weight, modifying diets, checking their sugars four times a day, taking pills/injecting insulin, and dealing with end-organ complications such as those with eyes, heart, kidneys, nerves, and stomach problems.

- The huge costs of diabetes are its secondary complications. For example, 44 percent of all dialysis patients are diabetics. At an average life expectancy of 5.7 years on dialysis at $73,000/year, this translates into nearly half a million dollars spent per diabetic patient on dialysis. For dialysis alone, this translates into $26 billion annually.

- Definitive treatment (voluntary weight loss) rarely succeeds. In spite of this, the weight loss industry has become a $61 billion industry. Bariatric surgery (weight loss surgery), is a major expense ($20,000 to $25,000 according to WebMD) and can have major complications. It is a last ditch effort in a severely morbidly obese individual and is now the most favorable option.

# Health Care: A Unique Market and Commodity

Because of its reliance on human cooperation, health care is a unique market with a unique commodity. This creates three major difficulties:

- Everyone benefits only when everyone participates; partial participation doesn't work. Hoarding health care for one person is of no benefit to that person. Diseases tend to strike individuals with the least amount of access and fewest resources. If not controlled, these diseases can greatly impact disease free individuals on both an economic and biological level.

- Health care requires subjective, often illogical, human decision-making. To be successful, this commodity cannot exist without an external authority that can and will make tough decisions that can seem cold and calculating.

- Health care is complex and not easy to define. No one, including patients, doctors, nurses, administrators, and government policy analysts, truly understands health care, disease, and the dying patient. When is someone sick? When is someone cured? What is the value of a particular treatment for society?

# Shalit Rule of Medical Treatment

Marc Shalit, professor of medicine at UCSF, believes that the number of treatments used in our arsenal for the sick individual is inversely proportional to the success of those treatments.

- When treatments are ineffective against an illness, we have many to choose from.

- When one treatment is successful, there is only one treatment—that treatment.

- The classic example is strep throat versus hiccups:

  » **Strep throat:** This requires a $4 course of penicillin that will cure bacterial tonsillitis 100 percent of the time. Other treatments need not be contemplated or even discussed.

  » **Hiccups:** Treatments are ineffective, so we see a list of hundreds of cures for hiccups. None of them are of great help.

- For a benign illness, such as hiccups, we laugh about our odd or even silly treatments that require unproven or even unconventional methods.

- For cancer, we do not laugh. We cry because of the serious nature of our failures. We present hundreds of expensive and dangerous treatments in a desperate attempt to cure a disease we do not fully understand.

- We then treat the side effects of the treatment, and health care costs rise exponentially. We further treat the side effects of the side effects, and costs go up even more for a multitude of treatments that offer slight or even no real advantage.

- Supporters of these treatments (drug companies, etc) then play on the emotions of family members and a vicious cycle of cost escalation occurs, leading to the "kitchen sink" mentality (let's try everything and anything and hope something, anything, works).

# The Major Conundrum for Health Care: Individual Rights Versus Societal Rights?

Perhaps the most troubling aspect of the health care industry is that it relies on the unanimous cooperation of patients to achieve success. No other industry relies on the cooperation of the commodity itself to achieve success. With mandatory cooperation critically necessary for success, the health care industry faces hurdles that other industries do not need to overcome. A quick overview of the problems is listed below, followed by four cases that exemplify, in increasing order of difficulty, why the period of the sociologically modern human is so problematic and why health care perfectly exemplifies the problems humanity faces at this time.

- To be successful against disease, we must have universal cooperation.

- However, this mandatory participation requires individuals to give up some of their freedoms.

- To give up freedoms, individuals must sign a social contract that is universal in all cultures.

- No longer can an individual be an innocent bystander in the Supercivilization and opt out, claiming that it is the responsibility of others to resolve problems.

- Vaccinations are one simple example whereby individuals who opt out endanger all of us. It is also an example of how we can efficiently and effectively move en mass unanimously to solve problems.

## Case 1. Typhoid Mary:
## Society Versus the Sociopathic Individual

Some cases are simple: individual rights and freedoms should be disregarded when society's interests are potentially in serious jeopardy. The case of Typhoid Mary is a classic example in which societal interests win:

- Mary Malone was a cook living in New York from 1900-1907 who carried typhoid fever (a bacteria residing in the gallbladder).

- At that time typhoid fever was a life-threatening disease that could be quite easily spread through oral and fecal secretions to other people.

- In 1906 when public health officials wanted blood samples from her, she refused to cooperate, citing prejudice.

- She was arrested and put into isolation against her will.

- She then agreed to cooperate after being imprisoned, and so was released. She then secretly resumed her duties as a cook, and then further infected 25 people.

- She was again arrested and put in permanent quarantine where she later died.

- Health officials argued that since she was knowingly putting others at risk and had little disregard for society that she should be isolated and even punished for her behavior. There was little disagreement.

## Case 2. HIV in the United States: Society Versus
## Societal Subculture

Some cases are less simple and require discussion. In the end, the case of Human Immunodeficiency Virus (HIV) and its spread among a group of individuals participating in group sex was more difficult to resolve. A group whose actions were "hurting no one" argued that individual freedoms supersede societal interests. The spread of HIV to society beyond the subculture in which it started shifted the issue to a large-scale societal issue.

- At the first signs of AIDS in the early 1980s, epidemiologists were concluding the spread of HIV was occurring because of sexual relations, including sexual intercourse, oral sex, and anal sex, engaged in by homosexual men.

- Mervyn Silverman, public health commissioner of San Francisco, had to decide whether to shut down bathhouses where people—predominantly men—met to engage in sexual relations. He decided to shut them down, in spite of many protests.

- Opponents of his decision argued these were willing participants who fully knew the risks they were engaging in. Supporters of bathhouses felt participants were really hurting no one but themselves: it was purely an individual choice. Since HIV was transmitted strictly through voluntary acts of questionable behavior (sexual intercourse, sharing needles, etc), those becoming infected were of little concern to the rest of society. They argue individual behaviors are truly not the government's business.

- Who, though, would pay for the cost of treating these sick individuals? Do these "private" acts really remain "private" as these supporters argue? Does one's behavior, no matter how "private," purely affect no other individuals? What about the HIV positive individual who lies to partners about his/her status and infects innocent individuals unaware of his status? What about the health care worker who must treat this individual and the risks these workers take against accidental exposures?

## Case 3. Tobacco and Alcohol Addiction: Society Versus Powerful Sub-Interests

Of even greater challenge is the question of behaviors that involve the use of substances. Should they be banned? Does the use of substances that are harmful to oneself truly affect no one?

- Alcohol and tobacco kills hundreds of thousands of people every year.

- The effects of their use are not always fatal (with tobacco, far more fatal in the long term; with alcohol, far more fatal in the short term).

- One substance has few if any negative effects on someone who uses it as intended (alcohol), while the other substance (tobacco) is harmful at any level of use.

- Most of these burdens are an indirect cost and not a direct cost for their use. The effects are subtle, yet real.

- These substances are interwoven into our cultural fabric. How do we eliminate something that has been a part of our culture for thousands (alcohol) or hundreds (tobacco) of years?

- Few people want these freedoms taken away because, for some users, there is little or no cost to society. Alcohol, for example, has no ill effects on someone who responsibly drinks a glass of wine a day.

- Even more problematic is the issue of power in society. Those people who are selling the substances have the power (that is, money) to convince the government to ignore the consequences that these substances have on society.

## Case 4. Individuals Refusing Care: Societal Interests Versus Individual Liberties

This is now the most difficult question that faces health care and humanity in general. Does society have the right to force individuals to be treated for any condition? Even if the condition has no seeming effect on others, do societal rights *always* trump individual rights? Here is a classic example:

- What do we do about the young man who is rock climbing, falls, hits his head, breaks a leg, and refuses treatment at the scene of the accident? He then returns to the hospital 24 hours later and has a subdural hematoma in his head and an open fracture that becomes infected. His delay causes him to be comatose the rest of his life, and the infection leads to several operations to save his leg. He will be on a ventilator for the rest of his life and undergo multiple operations on his leg. This will cost society millions of dollars.

- Do we force people who have no seeming danger or fallout to society to take treatment? Are we all willing participants (implied consent) from the time we are born into the Supercivilization, or are we forced to become participants against our will even if it takes a toll on all of us?

- What about this gentleman's right to rock climb? Does it matter if he is rock climbing with safety straps in a studio or on the face of El Capitan? It is not hurting anyone or is it? Do all behaviors require consent by society, even when they are seemingly benign?

What are the implications of this conundrum for society?:

- The fallout is growing rapidly in the Supercivilization; the fallout is the huge cost of his health care that will be paid by society and one reason why health care is growing at an alarming rate.

- If we force people to get treatment, we lose our effectiveness as physicians when our patients fear us rather than seek our help. This is an unfortunate conundrum for health care. It is an unfortunate conundrum for the Supercivilization.

- Isolated injuries are no longer isolated problems. Fixing these problems is a potentially massive expense for society. The individual is no longer making an isolated decision that focuses only on him/herself. In the Third Biosociophysical Era, there is no such thing as an individual making an isolated decision. All decisions currently impact all of humanity.

- The social realm is so fraught with gray areas (not so much black and white) that we stand little chance in seeking solutions to resolve our social problems.

# Our Chances with Disease?

As socialization becomes mandatory, so does the need to take care of others around us. What is wrong with that?

- The main problem with disease today isn't death; it is the burden of disease.

- Disease will never be a Class IV Event, because we understand how to keep people alive and understand the science.

- This understanding will drain resources when applied to the social realm.

- In a Swiss-cheese world, we will survive disease processes. In a planetary-formation world of the 21st century, disease burden will be the perfect cofactor to destroy the Supercivilization.

- With the *requirement* of universal cooperation to resolve these burdens, disease will be the perfect cofactor for a Class VIII Event.


# More Is Better in Health Care?

The assumption has always been that more health care—more doctors, nurses, hospitals for example—equals greater success. This is not necessarily true. Why?

- The United States consumes 50 percent of the world's prescription drugs, but has only 5 percent of the world's population.

- If our drugs are so beneficial, we would easily be the most well-adjusted, healthy citizenry in the world, but based upon objective statistics, we are not.

- We are merely average when objective statistics are used to compare our success to other nations.

- Our drugged-out culture of addition is being misled by an industry that cares more about profits than about its patients (see Figure 7.3).

- More is not always better, and there is a major mismatch in resources in this world (Figure 7.4). It is the misapplication of our resource base that is the greatest problem today. A culture of addition must be tempered by promoting a culture of subtraction.

- Those who suffer from too few resources live in the Second and Third World. Six out of the top ten diseases in the Second and Third World, measured in disability adjusted life years (DALYs), are a result of too few resources (Figure 7.4).

- Those who suffer from too many resources live in the First World. Six out of the top ten DALYs in the First World are because of—in part or in full—greater resource consumption.

- As a Supercivilization, our key to survival will be to focus on resource procurement and better-matched resources to existing areas of need and oversupply.

## How Do We Promote Human Welfare When Vested Interests Control the Medical Establishment?

Decisions about health care are never black and white, yet if we are going to progress, we need an overarching institution willing to make these decisions.

- We must have a third party that is divorced from the social environment to determine the efficacy of a therapy, drug, or treatment.

### Culture of addition

A culture that is supported by a decentralized system of government whereby individual interests support additive solutions to problems. Currently, humanity is primarily a culture of addition.

### Culture of subtraction

A culture that is supported by a more centralized, authoritative system of government whereby group interests support subtractive solutions to problems. When competition is centrally regulated and vested interests defending current goods and services (the status quo) have less power, these solutions become realistic alternatives.

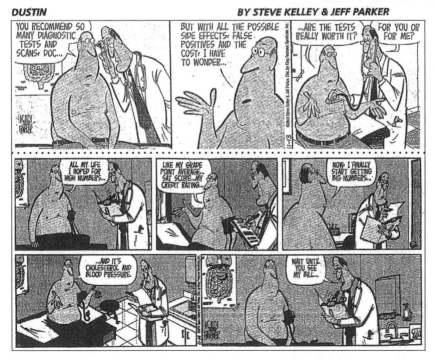

FIGURE 7.3    A Layperson's Cynical Look at the Current Health Care System

## Ten Leading Causes of Disease in Each Area of the World

| | High-Income Countries | | Middle- & Low-Income Countries |
|---|---|---|---|
| 1 | Ischemic Heart Disease (8.3)* | 1 | Perinatal Problems (6.4) |
| 2 | Cerebrovascular Accident (6.3) | 2 | Lower Respiratory Infections (6.0) |
| 3 | Depression (5.6) | 3 | Ischemic Heart Disease (5.2) |
| 4 | Alzheimers (5.0) | 4 | HIV (5.1) |
| 5 | Tracheobronchial Cancers (3.6) | 5 | Cerebrovascular Accident (4.5) |
| 6 | Hearing Loss (3.6) | 6 | Diarrhea (4.2) |
| 7 | Chronic Obstructive Pulmonary Disease (3.5) | 7 | Depression (3.1) |
| 8 | Diabetes (2.8) | 8 | Malaria (2.9) |
| 9 | Alcohol Use (2.8) | 9 | Tuberculosis (2.6) |
| 10 | Osteoarthritis (2.5) | 10 | Chronic Obstructive Pulmonary Disease (2.4) |

## Correlation of These Diseases to Resource Availability**

| Number of Top 10 Diseases in High-Income Countries | | Resource Availability | Number of Top 10 Diseases in Middle- & Low-Income Countries | |
|---|---|---|---|---|
| 0 | | Completely a result of too few resources | 6 | (1, 2, 4, 6, 8, 9) |
| 0 | | Partly a result of too few resources | 0 | |
| 4 | (3, 4, 6, 10)*** | No correlation to resource availability | 1 | (7) |
| 3 | (1, 2, 8) | Partly a result of too many resources | 2 | (3, 5) |
| 3 | (5, 7, 9) | Completely a result of too many resources | 1 | (10) |

   * Percentage of total disability-adjusted life years (DALYs) lost as a result of that illness in that area of the world. DALYs based on a 3 percent annual discount rate and uniform age weights.

  ** The author's estimate of the relative influence of resource availability on the impact of the disease processes above

 *** Numbers of the diseases listed above

FIGURE 7.4   Today's Diseases in Order of Disability-Adjusted Life Years (DALYs): A Comparison of Diseases and World Resource Availability in High-Income vs. Middle- and Low-Income Countries (2001)

- By default, the liberal democratic state is the only party that can oversee regulation objectively.

- Rather than limiting costs, the free market does the exact opposite by producing the illusion of need and *controlling information flow.*

- For example, as much money was spent on marketing sleep aids Lunesta and Ambien in a single year as the entire sleep research budget of the National Institutes of Health that same year.

## ADHD Is a Classic Case of Promoting an Illusion of Need

When vested interests are free to exploit the gray areas of the social realm, results will benefit a few, not the whole group. The classic case occurring now is the exploitation of the human psyche for the benefits of drug companies:

- Attention deficit hyperactivity disorder (ADHD) is diagnosed in 6.4 million Americans (mainly boys) between the ages of four and seventeen.

- Approximately 10 percent of all boys in the United States are prescribed either Adderall or Ritalin.

- Dr. Thomas Frieden, head of the CDC (Centers for Disease Control and Prevention), commented, "Misuse appears to be growing at an alarming rate."

- Use of these drugs is fueled by drug companies promoting medications to the general public. Drug companies are putting pressure on families to convince their doctors to prescribe the medication. Doctors prescribe it often to placate family wishes, not because of good science.

- This is hardly what Adam Smith had in mind in touting the benefits of the division of labor and the efficiency of markets.

CHAPTER 8

# Primarily Human-Induced Problems

"'...all appear right in their turn, even though they contradict each other.' The last comments point to the most obvious problem with adversarial debate: antagonists frequently resort to whatever techniques work to win."

—*Dane Scott and Blake Francis, editors of Debating Science: Deliberation, Values, and the Common Good*

# A Resource Problem We Face Today—Lack of Water

The depletion of resources is a huge problem for humanity today. Of specific concern are resources that allow us to subsist at our most basic level. One example is fresh water and its growing scarcity. Over the last two centuries water use has grown at twice the rate of the human population. The following facts are indicative of the problem:

- Just over a billion people have access to only a gallon of fresh water a day.

- About 2.6 billion people have access to only 5 gallons of fresh water a day.

- Half of the people in the developing world have disease associated with an inadequate water supply.

- Half of surface fresh water is being tapped and will increase to 70 percent by 2025.

- In twenty years, humanity's demand for fresh water will exceed the supply by 50 percent.

## Other Resource Problems

In addition to threatened fresh water supplies, our basic subsistence faces other threats:

- Three quarters of a metric ton of topsoil necessary for farming are lost per second.

- Five thousand acres of forest cover are lost per hour. Not only does this hurt the biosphere, but eliminates the commodities needed for building domicile structures.

- Forty thousand productive acres of farmland are being turned into barren land per day.

- By 2025, up to 3.6 billion people could be living in countries that cannot feed themselves because of low water availability, poor infrastructure, and unproductive farmland.

## Resource Problems: Their Foundation

In spite of these and other resource problems there really comes down to one resource that is fundamentally related to all these problems: energy. Energy, if used correctly, will serve as a foundation for the procurement and efficient utilization of other resources. If used carelessly, energy can undermine our existence. The energy problem now serves as a major problem for humanity. Why?

Two resource problems are special and underlay the success of the Supercivilization:

- **Fossil fuel shortages:** This is related to using too much of a good thing, as its supply vanishes.

- **Climate change:** This is related to using too much of a good thing, as its waste production overwhelms us.

This resource problem—unmitigated energy use—creates the flip side of the same toxic coin: too many humans using too many resources in a confined space called Earth.

We won against our environment in humanity's past, and now we are left with only ourselves as our major threat.

Our greatest challenge is not the natural environment, including other organisms we are competing with; it is ourselves that we now must deal with to survive.

## Too Much Discretionary Problem-Solving with Too Few Resources

Having too few resources is one thing. Having too few resources with too many people is not just exponentially more problematic, it is uniquely problematic to humanity today. We have never had this conundrum before involving all of humanity. The consequences of this predicament are as follows:

- There is an inverse relationship between the number of cerebral cortical neurons and available resources to maintain our standard of living (Figure 8.1).

- Energy is the fundamental resource causing this inverse relationship.

- If any particular commodity is in short supply, energy will be expended to either mine it, produce it synthetically, or create a substitute for it. Resource shortages are not the major problem for humanity.

- Fresh water can be created through energy-using desalinization plants, for example.

- Food shortages can always be resolved through manufacturing fertilizers for the soil and creating better irrigation techniques. Energy can improve this process exponentially.

Resource shortages will induce disorganized, uncoordinated, and dysfunctional social interaction. So many people will have so many solutions that unless an institution is in place to orchestrate the best solutions, the resource shortages will lead to the least effective solutions and eventually to a Class VIII Event.

Like a supernova that explodes as a result of the weight of waste accumulation, so too will the Supercivilization. As we expend more resources, particularly energy, to maintain our standard of living, thereby creating exponentially greater waste accumulation—especially in the form of carbon dioxide—we create this growing dissonance between solutions and human creativity.

## Climate Change Facts

Climate change is the end result of our growth as a species. It is, ironically, a product of our overwhelming success as a species. Yet, this problem is still unresolved because of social intransigence. Our institutions have not kept pace with our creativity. This has led to confusion, vitriol, and stasis that could lead to catastrophic self-annihilation. Here are the facts (Figures 8.2A to C, 8.3):

- If all $CO_2$ emissions were to totally stop now (currently atmospheric $CO_2$ is 401 ppm as of April 2014), Earth still will not have reached its final thermal state in the atmosphere; that will not come for decades.

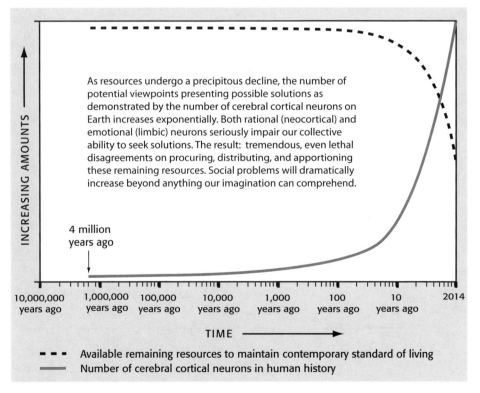

FIGURE 8.1    Resources Available to Sustain Our Contemporary Standard of Living and Total Number of Cerebral Cortical Neurons vs. Time (Conceptual Only)

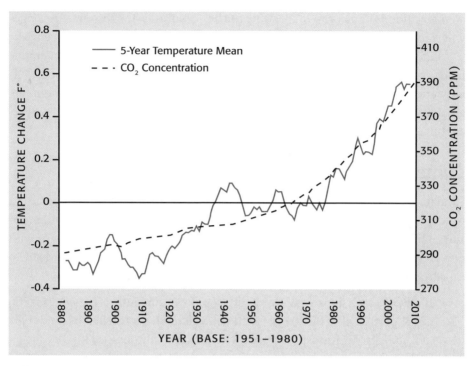

**FIGURE 8.2 A** Global Temperature Trend and Atmospheric $CO_2$ over the Last 130 Years

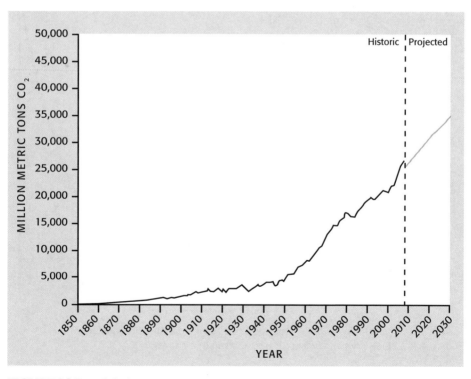

**FIGURE 8.2 B** Global $CO_2$ Emissions, 1850–2030
*Projections show continued massive increases …*

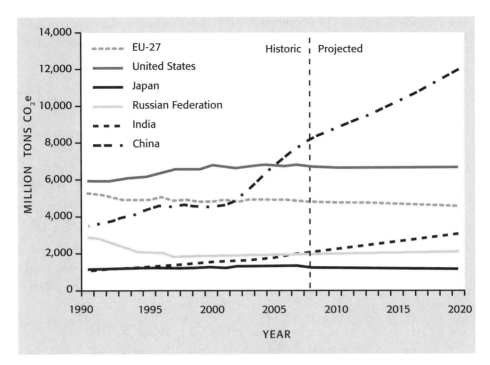

FIGURE 8.2 C   Millions of Tons of $CO_2$ Emitted by Selected Countries vs. the Year
*… with those increases being a result of rising standards of living for the developing world, primarily China and India. The developed world is stagnant.*

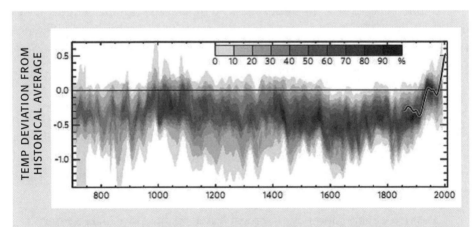

Northern Hemisphere temperature data from ten 21st-century studies of tree rings and a variety of other proxies are combined, with darker colors showing areas of greater agreement. The black line 1850–2000 shows temperatures recorded by thermometers. The "Little Ice Age" of early modern times is evident in nearly all studies. A "Medieval Warm Period" around 100 AD is found in some studies but not others. In the less complete data (not shown) for the Southern Hemisphere, the Little Ice Age is apparent but not a Medieval Warm Period.

FIGURE 8.3   Rise in Atmospheric Temperature over Past 1,300 Years

- Despite mandating limits through the Kyoto protocol, anthropogenic $CO_2$ production has risen 80 percent since its adoption (21 to 38 gigatonnes annually) in 1997. It has been a complete failure.

- Since this Kyoto adoption, we have globally emitted one-quarter of all $CO_2$ produced in the atmosphere since 1750.

- We have globally produced as much $CO_2$ in the last thirty-four years as we have in the previous 220.

- We have seen a global atmospheric temperature rise of 0.8°C since the mid-19th century.

- Atmospheric temperatures didn't start rising until one hundred years after the rise in $CO_2$.

- A dose response curve is unmistakable between $CO_2$ and atmospheric temperatures. Near unanimous consensus has been obtained in the scientific community.

- Merely a 2°C rise in temperatures projected to occur by 2100 would beat any sustained rate of rise that civilized humans (last 12,000 years) have ever seen.

The Intergovernmental Panel on Climate Change (IPCC) is conservatively estimating that $CO_2$ could rise 6.4°C by the end of this century, but some climatologists are projecting a rise as high as 11°C.

A difference of 6°C in atmospheric temperatures (global temperatures of 21°C versus 15°C today), as projected by the IPCC, is the same difference (global temperatures of 9°C) that brought glaciation as far south as New York City tens of thousands of years ago.

## Climate Change: Our Greatest Fears

Climate change is extremely dangerous because our best scientists still do not know enough about the Earth to say with absolute certainty which potential problems climate change can bring to humanity. Here is what scientists worry about most:

- Positive feedback loops are the most feared result. As we increase our $CO_2$, we create positive feedback loops that affect other variables. These loops will rapidly increase $CO_2$ and temperature change in the atmosphere by serving as a self-perpetuating runaway greenhouse. Further human release of $CO_2$ will not be the only factor causing an increase of atmospheric $CO_2$; the Earth will do it itself. Five potentially major feedback loops to cause the most danger to us are as follows:

The Supercivilization: Essential Concepts

» Oceans will stop buffering $CO_2$ and atmospheric temperature change. The ocean has been a major buffer (Figure 8.4) by absorbing 50 times the amount of $CO_2$ released into the atmosphere. The oceans are beginning to acidify causing changes to marine life, and most importantly, discouraging further absorption of $CO_2$. Oceans have also buffered atmospheric temperature by absorbing most of the heat generated by the increased radiation absorption by $CO_2$. Oceans have had a steadier rise in temperature for the last 150 years than the atmosphere, which has been increasing recently.

» Increased humidity in the air will lead to additional infrared radiation absorption. As heat is produced in the oceans and atmosphere, relative humidity rises. Sixty percent of atmospheric warming is a result of water in the air; only 25 percent is because of $CO_2$.

» More $CO_2$ will be released from sequestered areas as a result of heating. Permafrost from the northern continents and methane hydrates from the ocean bottoms could dramatically increase atmospheric warming without a human presence. Over 90 percent of the permafrost (900 billion tons of $CO_2$ currently are sequestered) could be released before the end of this century given enough warming. Trillions of tons of methane hydrates exist at the bottom of the oceans, and when warmed, those hydrates can cause a massive release of methane which is another greenhouse gas that produces warming (Figure 8.5).

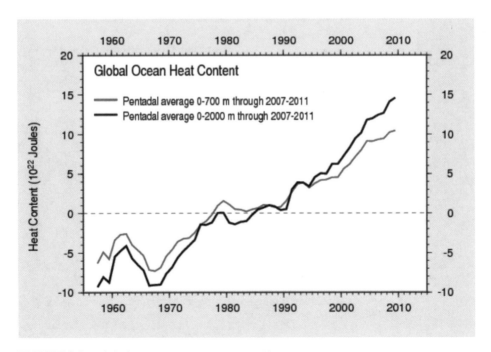

FIGURE 8.4   Global Ocean Heat Content vs. Time

» Change in the biosphere can lead to increased heating. As we replace the rain forests and other $CO_2$ absorbing areas, we increase the $CO_2$ in the atmosphere. At 3°C the biosphere is projected to become a net producer of $CO_2$ because of both chlorophyll production that decreases in the oceans and decreased algae production (6.3 percent reduction since recent warming began in oceans).

» Decreased reflectivity (albedo) because of warming will send less radiation back into space. The most reflective areas of Earth (alpine glaciers at the equatorial regions) will melt and as a result, more reflectivity will allow for less retained heat to remain in the atmosphere. Snow and ice have one-sixth the absorption that bare Earth soil has. There has been an 18 percent reduction in the surface area of moderate latitude glaciers between 1985 and 1999.

Without significant changes in our $CO_2$ emissions, we will see dramatic increases in atmospheric $CO_2$ in the next few years. There is a projected increase of global $CO_2$ emissions from 31 gigatonnes in 2009 to 52 gigatonnes in 2040 if reductions are not made. Mere population growth and rising economies in the Second and Third World is enough to create dangerous increases in atmospheric $CO_2$.

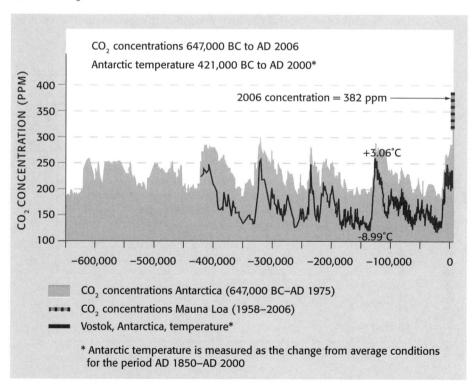

FIGURE 8.5   Changes in Carbon Dioxide and Atmospheric Temperature over the Last Several Hundred Thousand Years

The Supercivilization: Essential Concepts

# Irrationality of Opposed Vested Interests: Emotion Overriding Logic

It was the OJ Simpson verdict in 1994 that showed emotion can win over logic in the mind of a human. OJ Simpson was found not guilty of murdering his wife and her boyfriend. Prosecutors had plenty of evidence showing OJ Simpson was the murderer, yet Simpson's attorneys used emotion and obfuscation to convince the jury of his innocence. They focused on interracial animosity (Simpson is African American and his wife and her boyfriend were white) to bring focus on other issues besides the evidence. His case reflects a similar argument for climate change:

- All questions posed in the inanimate world have answers. We merely need to investigate our empirical world to find those answers to our questions. Many times we choose not to ask the question or even search for the answer.

- No questions posed in the social realm have universal answers; we create our own answers to the questions that we pose.

- Arguments are not objective in the social realm. They are completely subjective, which makes no argument in the social realm a clearly objective yes-or-no battle.

- Because arguments are never black or white, they rely on interpretation. The best arguments in debates are often the least logical.

- Solutions to problems are rarely 100 percent correct in the social realm. There usually are losers, but those losers are manipulated in the following ways: they don't know they have lost; they know they lost, but don't care; or they do not have the power to fight for the changes that caused them to lose.

- The social realm means reality is determined by power and not objective evidence. The questions we pose are chosen by whomever has control of society and its agenda.

- Solutions are largely determined by the herd effect, and whoever controls the herd effect, controls the answers to our questions.

- We usually weigh particular evidence out of convenience when it fits our situation, and so our preconceived notions can become validated even when they are wrong.

The argument on climate change parallels the OJ Simpson prosecution failure in three important ways:

- By their very nature, scientists are not allowed to debate an issue using irrational, emotive arguments, and therefore they often lose in the court of public opinion.

- Scientists are reluctant to embrace their logical theories in public because of a fear of backlash by superiors and politicians controlling these scientists' salaries and grants.

- Powerful emotive counterarguments and personal circumstances mitigate reason. We all want to live long and prosperous lives. That is a value, not a fact.

## Herd effect
Our willingness to respond to something based on the reactions of others to the same stimulus.

# Silicon Breast Implant Case

Like the OJ Simpson case, the silicon breast implant case showed how debates today are won and lost. The winning argument is typically predicated more on the size of the armamentarium rather than the veracity of a debate. An overview of the court case follows:

- In 1984, jurors awarded $211,000 in compensatory and $1.5 million in punitive damages to a woman who had immune system disorders "caused" by her breast implants.

- Several "experts" were paraded in front of the jury claiming that the breast implants caused the immune problems. Several experts had conflict-of-interest issues as they promoted their own views to further their financial interests.

- Little evidence was available at that time to support claims by the "experts." Jurors were forced to make decisions on a science they had no basic understanding of.

- Those interests that had the most to lose or win made the biggest efforts to promote their view, even if the view was counterproductive for society in general.

- It took two decades to conduct the best science to refute all the misconceptions related to these breast implants. Over $4.25 billion was awarded in a settlement before anyone could say for sure that these breast implants were totally benign.

The same problem occurs today with climate change: by the time we definitively convince all the doubters, it will be too late, and a self-perpetuating greenhouse effect could occur. The damage could become irreversible before scientists categorically prove to skeptics a relationship exists between human $CO_2$ emissions and climate change.

The only way to win against these vested interests is to make sure everyone is sufficiently—and quickly—educated. The power of these smaller interests should not grow sufficiently large at the expense of dooming the Supercivilization.

## Fossil Fuels Created the Supercivilization

The relationship between energy and the development of human civilization is quite strong. Here are the facts of biological systems, such as the Supercivilization, that grow quickly:

- Ninety percent of human population growth has occurred in the last 350 years. This period coincides with the Industrial Revolution.

- The previous 4 million years were most likely marked by periods of slow growth, die-offs, and then slow growth again.

- The past 350 years appears to be slow and steady growth, but in actuality it is massive and exponential growth.

The bell shaped distribution curve of growing biological systems (growth rate versus the total number of systems) tends to favor most systems that grow at a moderate pace. These systems exist in the middle or fat portion of this normal curve. Why? Those systems with moderate success last the longest. Those that have little success fail because they are subject to chance catastrophic events (natural events outside their control) before they firmly establish themselves. Those that have the most success outgrow their resource base quickly and starve themselves of resources.

# The Period of Exponential Growth Is Over

Our global population growth rates have been as high as 3 percent annually. Today it is 1.19 percent. This growth is unsustainable. Why?

- The period of exponential population growth since the Industrial Revolution must come to an end, because our society is unable to establish the institutions necessary to cope with the rapidly growing ICQ/ITQ.

- Our culture must change to reflect this new value system. It still does not. The countries of Europe and Russia that are seeing labor shortages are still calling for more births. There are still calls for more drilling to match fossil fuel use with our growth rate.

- We are very dependent on our scientific advancements that allow us to sustain our growth, but science is breaking down because of our advancing social world. Social pathology will no longer allow us to obtain the solutions we need in resolving these problems. Most of our problems are social problems, not natural problems, and the solutions to social problems are exponentially more difficult to resolve.

Seemingly "natural" problems such as climate change will not be resolved until our culture changes first. Climate change is really a cultural problem not a geophysical or meteorological problem. To change our culture, our institutions must match our ideas of maximizing our scientific advancement along with slower or even zero population growth.

## Infrastructure Changes and Shalit's Rule Generalized

Massive new infrastructure changes (both energy and social) will be necessary to resolve climate change and resource depletion issues. As Shalit's Rule (the less successful the treatments are for a medical condition, the more treatments there are, the more wasteful they become in resource use, and the less effective they are) is generalized to the human predicament, we see the development of more infrastructures of other far less efficient energy sources that gradually become more difficult to procure.

- Our Supercivilization is fixated on fossil fuels because they are cheap, easy, and so successful. Why change? In the 20th century this was a rhetorical question, but today it is a vital one.

- We have few alternatives to fossil fuels today because our primary solution (oil) created a gigantic infrastructure for delivery of this product to the consumer. As a result, other forms of energy development were discouraged. Vested interests who control the US Congress, the President, and other governments around the world, discouraged other infrastructure development because it would hurt their profits. Little was done in the twentieth century.

- A smorgasbord of alternatives (such as Robert Socolow and Stephen Pacala's chart presented in *Science* in 2004 showing multiple sources of energy to replace oil) means disaster, not success (Shalit's Rule). When we see a variety of solutions we see very poor solutions that are partial, inefficient, and unreliable.

Because we have yet to see one simple, inexpensive solution to replace fossil fuels, we are in serious trouble. One solution would be good because it would allow for cost scalability and greater efficiencies. Currently, nothing can compete with fossil fuels and if we had something, it would have occurred already. Replacing this fossil fuel infrastructure with one just as successful will take decades. That could doom us, given our dire need for immediate solutions because of climate change.

We are in for a very bumpy ride in our Golden Hour, as meeting an 85 percent reduction in carbon emissions by 2040 is virtually impossible if we want to sustain our standard of living at its current level. Our reliance on science rather than changing our institutions to create a new culture to solve this problem could be our death knell. Science breaks down in high ICQ/ITQ environments.

## Social Problems Resulting from Small Energy Mismatches Can Lead to Meltdowns

It doesn't take much to cause social breakdown when the primary source of our success (energy) is depleted. Near the turn of the century, California suffered from mismanagement and delays in infrastructure development that matched the increased use of electricity because of demand from computer use. An overview of the events is as follows:

- Small mismatches of a few percentage points between energy production and consumption can lead to disaster. Costs skyrocketed and rolling blackouts and brownouts were seen around the year 2000, especially in California.

- Between 1988 and 1997 energy transmission investment fell 0.8 percent per annum and maintenance investment fell 3.3 percent per annum. This led to infrastructure inadequacy.

- During the same period, electricity demand, because of Internet use, increased 2.4 percent per annum.

- Deregulation of the energy market with the empowerment of malevolent companies like Enron also led to major energy disruptions. Enron was exploiting a market that had little oversight and made millions by purposely withholding energy from utilities to drive the cost up.

Without adequate institutions in place to monitor these malevolent interests, resource depletion can become catastrophic. Supply and demand is compromised when those holding the cards (that is, those who have ownership of the means of production) can manipulate the markets they control.

## Major Energy Infrastructure Problem: Cost

While vested interests promote their commodity and the infrastructure it requires, the shift to another commodity also requires new infrastructure costs. Here are the numbers:

- According to American Society of Civil Engineering, the cost just to fix the deferred maintenance in our current energy infrastructure would be $2.2 trillion.

- Infrastructure changes necessary just to create a Smart Grid for solar and wind energy would be $400 billion over 10 years.

- Some estimates place a complete conversion to a new non-fossil fuel grid at $2 trillion.

## Illusion of Stability in Our Energy Infrastructure

We have become convinced that the Supercivilization can go on with fossil fuels indefinitely. We deem partial solutions as true solutions, but they are merely pseudosolutions. Why are we so shortsighted?

- Like our view of population growth, humans cannot see the past very well and the future is even less clear.

- We are led to believe our energy sources are stable, because that is what vested interests want us to believe. We are anything but stable. The larger we grow as a Supercivilization, the more dire our circumstances, and the more subject we are to the propaganda of wishful thinking.

- Vested interests have us looking at their individual problems only as a Class IV Event and not integrated as a Class VIII Event because it benefits them to give us all this illusion of stability.

- The situation doesn't look so dire when we isolate each problem and call it an independent issue. The impacts that the solutions create aren't

The Supercivilization: Essential Concepts

elaborated and quantified, but merely simplistically explained.

- Those problem solvers that best know the industries, and the impacts they will have, are vested in the industry itself, making their analyses at best questionable.

In a highly interconnected world such as the Supercivilization, these independent problems are not as easily isolated. The impacts can be massive. Two examples are antibiotic use in medicine and fracking's impact on climate change. The impacts are slow, but progressively more expensive and insidious, in spite of our initial elation over their discovery.

Carbon sequestration is a potential solution, but like the two examples above it is problematic:

- Carbon sequestration raises electricity generation costs by at least 30 percent.

- Our ability to generate energy at such a small price for the near term is going to be inordinately more difficult to resolve in the long term.

Even though fracking for natural gas, tar sands development (33 percent of energy generated is used to help refine it), and shale are potential solutions to the energy resource depletion, all become progressively more expensive.

Costs to the environment are major unknowns. As we reach to deeper areas (deep sea drilling as in the Deepwater Horizon accident), inclement areas (drilling on the North Slope of Alaska), and use additional techniques to reach

## Smart Grid

A modernized electrical grid that uses analog or digital information and communications technology to gather and act on information. This information about suppliers and consumers can be used in an automated fashion to improve the efficiency, reliability, economics, and sustainability of the production and distribution of electricity.

harder-to-extract areas (North Sea drilling costs $10 to extract oil whereas Saudi Arabia costs $2 for every barrel of oil), we are riddled with questions. No one can put an accurate price on these costs.

## The Unfortunate Facts About Fossil Fuels

The sad reality is that our growth as a Supercivilization is greatly impacting our ability to continue using fossil fuels. Here are the facts (Figures 8.6, 8.7, 8.8):

- Currently the United States gets 86 percent of its energy from fossil fuels.

- Just nine countries control 950 billion of the remaining 1100 billion barrels of global oil reserves.

- Five fossil fuel sources remain (in their order of convenience):

  » **Oil:** 2.1 trillion barrels in proven global reserves have existed; we have used about half so far. The USGS projected in 2000 3.012 trillion barrels remain but Kenneth Deffeyes projects that 2.013 trillion remain. At roughly 40 billion barrels of oil used per year, this fuel will be depleted in 20–30 years.

  » **Natural gas:** Fracking is the hope, but only reduces $CO_2$ emissions by 40 percent compared to coal. This issue resolves only resource depletion without significantly affecting climate change solutions. Thus it is a Class IV solution not a Class VIII.

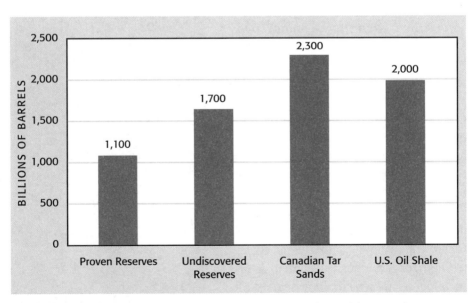

**FIGURE 8.6**   World Oil Resources as of 2006 (Billions of Barrels)

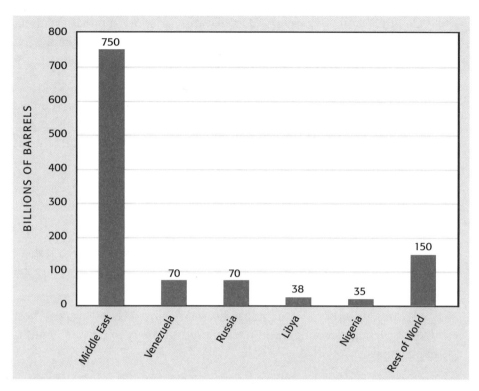

**FIGURE 8.7** World Proven Reserves in Billions of Barrels by Country (2006)

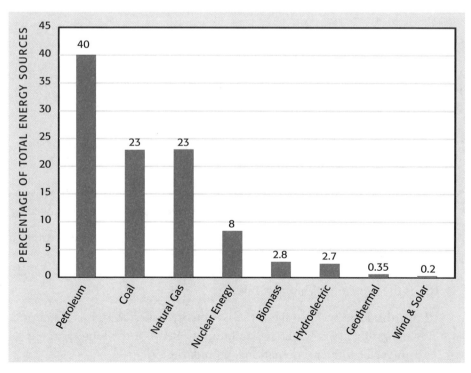

**FIGURE 8.8** Energy Sources (Percentage of Total) for the United States (2006)

» **Coal:** Costs to sequester $CO_2$ make this far more dubious. Without sequestration, its use is over. It is of virtually unlimited supply, but other compounds of emissions make this extremely problematic for the environment.

» **Tar sands:** Costs to refine and sequester $CO_2$ are expensive, and unless sequestration happens, tar sands extraction will be highly problematic. There is a huge supply that can be refined into crude oil, but it still has $CO_2$ emissions' problems as problematic as coal.

» **Shale:** This is the most expensive to refine and sequester $CO_2$ based on current knowledge. On top of these costs, there are many unknowns about its refining process and costs on a large scale.

- As a result of rising demand from a larger Supercivilization, even if there are better, more efficient uses of resources, we will still be faced with rising prices, extraction costs, and environmental costs.

- Paul Bures, expert on the oil industry, says we have 50 to 60 years at most of oil use left, given our current rates of use and ability to tap into deposits more efficiently.

- By 2019, oil production will be down to 90 percent of its peak oil production from 2005.

# Natural Gas: Our Savior?

As of late, natural gas seems like the solution to our energy problem. It is not. These are the facts that support the idea of natural gas being the solution:

- Daniel Yergin, oil expert, has called it a "game changer."

- Natural gas releases just over half the $CO_2$ per amount of energy generated compared to coal and 74 percent of gasoline.

- There are seventy more years of natural gas for the United States if we converted suddenly to fracking natural gas to meet our entire energy needs.

- The United States can be a net exporter of natural gas by 2020 according to EIA and energy sufficient by 2035 using fracking.

This is the problem with that thinking:

- If one thinks in terms only of the US energy issues, then it is a solution. We must think as a Supercivilization now, because the long term effects are universal and have no national boundaries.

- Thinking of the energy problem as a Class IV problem and not a Class VIII problem will doom us.

- We are only decreasing the $CO_2$ output slightly but increasing demand through population growth, making this a tradeoff at best and a dangerous procrastination at worst.

- At first natural gas appears to be a cheaper, cleaner alternative to oil, but is it really?

  » Fracking costs have unknown long term expenses and unknown ecological effects. Methane release could be significant.

  » The costs to the environment are only mitigated and not eliminated. $CO_2$ is still produced in large quantities, especially if our rate of use increases.

  » Infrastructure will have to change to match this new type of fossil fuel use. That is not without expense.

  » Money used to change the infrastructure could be used for other sources that do not do as much harm to the environment.

## Commitments Generate Success But at a Huge Monopolistic Price

The major problem with the Supercivilization is that economic success creates efficiencies but also creates monopolies.

- While we must commit to one technology to save on costs (Shalit's Rule), we create fewer options, thereby making us more susceptible to vested interests, their monopolistic practices, and control of the US legislature.

- Nuclear energy is a classic example of an industry competing with oil. We overlook the horrible effects of oil, because we have been infected with a paradigm (or prion) of acceptance. We know oil well and know little about nuclear power, so we are more comfortable with the ill effects of oil. At its optimum, nuclear energy can generate electricity as low as 1.72 cents/kw-hr. This is well below fossil fuels. With construction delays, that figure can rise tenfold quite easily. One delay on the building of nuclear power plant can add $6 to $10 billion onto its cost. This makes other forms of energy uncompetitive strictly because of social factors.

It is assumed that carbon sequestration will eventually resolve the $CO_2$ emissions problem. It is unproven technology now projected to increase energy costs by 30 percent because of new technologies. Do we actually have these in hand today? Our reliance on industry experts to guide policy and assume success before it has happened could be a major problem. Conflicts of interest are extremely problematic, as we saw in the housing bubble. For example, even if $CO_2$ sequestration is possible, what are the long term effects of the sequestration? Will it really add just 30 percent to the price of energy?

## Do We Need to Be Shocked to Be Driven Into Action?

Many theorists argue that it will take a "shock" to change the necessary sources of energy and the entire infrastructure. This doesn't have to be. Why?

- Naomi Klein argues that a "shock" is always necessary to disrupt the world order and make change seem necessary. She argues, though, that in a free market system, these shocks inevitably benefit the wealthiest individuals.

- As our expenditures (time and resources) for sustaining our standard of living increase, the less free time we have and the less likely we are to expend the necessary capital to resolve problems. We become painted into a corner.

- To get out of this conundrum, some theorists believe the future needs to be so tremendously negative (a die-off of millions to billions) before vested interests are willing to act.

- Americans are so preoccupied with our success with fossil fuels that we have had absolutely no reason to expend capital to create new infrastructure.

- We necessarily have to take our blinders off and see such a dangerous threat to usurp the powers of those who control the means of production.

- Die-offs are almost inevitable because of the gridlock from vested interests.

- The only way to avoid a shock is to wrestle power from vested interests that put products over people. The wealthy merely withdraw their capital, freeze markets, and ride out the "shock" until markets return later. Vested interests don't yet realize that this shock to the Supercivilization will doom them too.

By putting institutions in place that create a greater good for all of humanity, we can take our blinders off and see the major problems. This requires acknowledgment of the Supercivilization and institutions such as a global government that will help us avoid the ultimate catastrophe—a major die off.

# Resource Depletion: Advantages of Addressing a Primarily Human-Induced Event

All is not hopeless in the climate change and resource depletion catastrophes. There are pluses to consider regarding the resource depletion catastrophe, when compared to the purely human-induced catastrophe.

- Purely and primarily natural events rely on natural systems to guide us in our solutions. We fight these systems which unify humanity and create a bond to allow us to solve our problems. Climate change and resource depletion can still form this common bond, but only when conditions become so abysmally bad (usually a die-off) that humanity coordinates and cooperates. This is primarily because of the intransigent vested interests.

- Climate change and resource depletion can be prognosticated and operate on a predictable timetable, unlike purely human-induced events. As situations deteriorate for all of humanity, we will become motivated to resolve our differences and unify to defeat a huge disaster. It is not a hard concept to understand once our culture is accepting of the science.

- The timetable for success is clear. Greenhouse gas emissions need to be capped by 2015 and reduced by 85 percent by 2050 at the very latest (I argue earlier—2040) according to most scientists.

Chapter 9

# Purely Human-Induced Problems

"But Washington needs to understand that generating international public support for its view of the world is a core element of power, not merely an exercise in public relations. … In an increasingly empowered and democratized world, in the long run, the battle of ideas is close to **everything**."

—*Fareed Zakaria, author of* The Post-American World

# The Birth of the Supercivilization

At the beginning of the 21st century the Supercivilization is born. The Third Biosociophysical Era becomes a reality and humans' primary threat is ourselves.

- Self-interest and societal interests are not always congruent today because of a paradox of individual power. In the past with an expanding resource base, this congruency was more likely. This is no longer true, as a zero-sum game of material acquisition requires losers and winners.

- For the first time, our individual actions can instantaneously affect all of humanity, making our interconnectedness a key variable in our sustainability as a species.

- Our fundamental problem is not natural disaster, disease, or resource depletion but resource distribution and emotions stoked by these disparities.

- We cannot escape the anger and dissatisfaction of the masses of individuals who can now see this disparity with greater transparency.

- We must change from "us" and "them" to an "us" only. Our survival as a species depends on this.

- The world will not survive the onslaught of human emotions when disagreements tear at the basic fabric of our existence. Controlling, not eliminating, these emotions will be our key. We must maximize our use of our emotions to promote the general good, not merely the individual good.

- The disadvantaged of the Second and Third World can and will hold the entire Supercivilization hostage through blackmail. If they feel their situation is so grim that it is worthwhile to improve their conditions through any means, no matter how horrific, they will do so. It is this very situation that puts the Supercivilization at most risk for a catastrophic self-annihilation.

- In the past, people living in the areas of wealth hibernated in and exploited the poorer areas by controlling the world's agenda. Now, the agenda can be controlled by a very small disenfranchised minority because of the paradox of individual power.

- Many of the commodities that made the world great, particularly oil, are now in the hands of the disenfranchised (Third World) who were ignored in the 20th century. Because the infrastructure for these commodities still resides primarily in the First World, there is a potential powder keg of animosity as exploitation becomes more transparent to the disadvantaged.

# Increased Behavioral Pathology?

Does the Supercivilization have more social pathology than in the past? Or is it merely our perception that we have more social pathology than we really do? It isn't that the Supercivilization's existence is problematic, but that the potential social problems that the Supercivilization can bring are now potentially self-annihilating. It is not a question of whether social pathology exists; it is a question of the resonating effects of that pathology.

- Steven Pinker has pointed out that these times are among the most peaceful in recorded human history; actual pathology is not the problem. The perception of pathology is the problem.

- Declining resource bases, increased interconnectedness, disparities in wealth, and the potential technological firepower available to the average individual have made this world particularly (and historically speaking) dangerous for our species.

- To counter the intense and massive aspects of human emotions that will overtake our environment, we must think of ourselves as a Supercivilization .

- We must be taught that the Supercivilization is a living, breathing organism that must come first or else we will see its death very quickly through resonating behavioral pathology.

- This new paradigm, or prion, as I call it, must be instilled *in all of us and by all of us* before we annihilate ourselves. If not, we might have a prion imposed on us by a minority group whose interest is solely their own. (Prions are defined on page 45 and further discussed on page 165.)

- While every person is required to sign a social contract (it is mandatory for our survival in the 21st century), the critical aspect will be to coordinate the indoctrination of everyone and to convince everyone to become a willing participant in the Supercivilization.

# The Best Model for Our Survival

Perhaps the best way to compare the three greatest social theorists— Max Weber, Karl Marx, and Émile Durkheim—is to look at their unit of focus. Weber focused on the individual as the unit of power, Marx on class, and Durkheim on the entirety of society and its functional nature on our psyche. Whose model is most applicable today? All three were right in some ways, yet today we are left with a fundamental problem that none of the three could predict: the need to deal with exponential growth of our interconnectedness and the need to deal with a possible endpoint (self-annihilation) for society.

- Weber argues that the power of society resides in ideas of the mind and not necessarily the material environment. He argues we created a system that eventually smothers our creativity and enchains us within an "iron cage." Weber was resigned to the notion that rationalization was the inevitable growth of humanity, and there was no way to combat its growth. We become prisoners of our own environment, as our freedoms to express our ideas become neutered by a bureaucracy without values.

- Marxist ideology presupposes the power of the environment over our psyche or what Marx described as historical materialism. This determinism led to capitalism and the development of class and its eventual overthrow. His model is extremely rigid and not completely accurate, because conflict is not inevitable. If conflict is used to resolve issues today, we will destroy ourselves and waste our remaining resources very quickly. Unlike Marxist doctrine, I believe there is simply no definitive future; it is unpredictable and subject to our free will, not some predetermined path external to us.

- Durkheim's functional model of the organism is perhaps the best model today that will sustain human existence. He argues that society serves an important function and we all serve a functional role for society. We currently are part of a living, breathing organism in which every individual has the potential to turn cancerous or pathological and undermine society's (currently the Supercivilization's) survival. Durkheim believes dealing with our own unpredictability is our key to survival and creating order to resolve this pathology is paramount. The weakness of Durkheim's model is his view that the organismal integrity of society supersedes individual exploitation.

The 21st century is unique in that these three models are all correct and incorrect. A new view of society must take place because social conditions are now unique and we face problems never before experienced in the past: high interconnectedness, transparent disparities in wealth, and a declining resource base. We are becoming dangerously more rational to the point that we blindly accept our exploitation by vested interests as inevitable, mathematically based laws of a preconceived universe. We have free will and can rise above our exploitation (Marxist exploitation by vested interests) if we all simultaneously accept Durkheim's model of society (which I call the Supercivilization) and consciously create a Weberian culture of cooperation and unity.

We will encounter several types of social pathology (or social metaphors) that we must resolve to continue functioning optimally as a Supercivilization (Figure 9.1):

- **Monosystem and multisystem organ failure:** This pathology occurs at the level of our institutions, especially the state.

- **Protozoa and worms:** These occur at the level of political leaders/parties who live off the organism's livelihood. They slowly suck the life out

| | Multisystem Organ Failure | Worms | Protozoa |
|---|---|---|---|
| *Level of Pathology* | Macroculture/nations | Governments | Leaders |
| *Number of Individuals* | Millions to billions | Thousands | Dozens to hundreds |
| *Declaration Status* | Openly | Openly | Openly |
| *Main Reasons for Pathology* | Poor economics, resource depletion, prion conflict | Multisystem organ failure | Multisytem organ failure |
| *Methods to Counter Pathology* | Strong single prion, Western liberal democracy, strong scientific methodology | No multisystem organ failure | No multisystem organ failure |
| *Potential Long-Term Benefits from Pathology (Redeeming Values if Any)* | Neogenesis and ultimate development of Supercivilization | Evolving new prions and institutions after illness (rising immunity) | Evolving new prions and institutions after illness (rising immunity) |

FIGURE 9.1 Social Pathology of the Supercivilization (Metaphorical Organs and Organisms)

The Supercivilization: Essential Concepts

of the organism without destroying it. They drain the resources with an insidious effort for self-benefit.

- **Bacteria:** This occurs at the level of terrorist groups who take advantage of weakened institutions. They totally destroy the organism for self-gain and publicly acknowledge their opposition to the life of the Supercivilization.

- **Viruses:** This occurs at the level of surreptitious terrorist groups who silently live off a weakened organism waiting to explode in unison to announce themselves publicly with a vengeance. It is only after this incubation period does the Supercivilization succumb to this organism.

- **Prions:** These occur at the level of the mind. This is the most dangerous pathology: the ideas that reside in our consciousness. If we are without a collective consciousness and instead our consciousness is manipulated by a small minority who control our minds for their personal benefit, unprecedented disaster can occur. These organisms can be potentially good as well as bad, depending on the prion and who controls it. If we all safely and carefully control the prion, we ourselves create irrefutable

| Bacteria | Viruses | Prions |
|---|---|---|
| Groups | Groups | Ideas/paradigms |
| Dozens to millions | Unknown | Dozens to billions |
| Openly | Undeclared until very last moment | Open but unconsciously subscribed |
| Multisystem organ failure | Multisystem organ failure and new technology | Conflicting prions; dangerous, irrational prions |
| No multisystem organ failure | No multisystem organ failure | Strong all-encompassing single prion |
| Evolving new prions and institutions after illness (rising immunity) | Evolving new prions and institutions after illness (rising immunity) | Evolution of prion of universe centricity |

benefit for all; if it is controlled by a small minority, it can lead to a partial or total die-off.

Each of the pathologies are described below.

# Monosystem and Multisystem Organ Failure

Monosystem failure can quickly lead to multisystem organ failure as a result of our interconnectedness today. Several macrocultures—American, European, Russian, Chinese, Indian, Japanese, Latin—that dominate the Supercivilization and comprise unique value systems have separate norms, laws, and political systems.

Isolated institutions *without accountability* now exist that allow for organ failure. Here is a description of how that affects the Supercivilization:

- When a government is corrupt and dysfunctional, its effects can undermine the entire Supercivilization both directly and indirectly through blackmail, war, and terrorism (Soviet Union, China, Syria, Iran, North Korea).

- The Supercivilization has the potential to regenerate new organs or political systems. In the past these systems were independent and died out with little effect on other cultures. There was no regeneration. Today, the ideas, fears, and disease are shared, and a common culture exists, but is currently not recognized or acknowledged.

- In the Supercivilization today, we have the unique ability to avert meltdowns and die-offs of our subcivilizations at the expense of placing additional burdens on the rest of the subcivilizations. As we spread the risk, we make micromeltdowns less common, but on the other hand, we make multisystem organ failure far more likely (for example, the 2008 real estate and banking collapse).

- If a critical organ or government fails (for example, the US Government), the organism can fail. If smaller institutions fail, it can also translate into a multisystem failure leading to global failure (for example, the Greek economic meltdown).

- Without a global government to regulate these wide economic and political swings, there is less dimming capability and more volatility. Therefore more domino effects are inevitable.

Currently treatment is limited, given nation-state sovereignty.

# Protozoa and Worms

Individuals and political parties can suck the life blood out of the Supercivilization. How this happens is as follows:

- Institutions or parties (worms) or individuals (protozoa) hold positions of power. They do not accept the premise of the Supercivilization and will use their power to persuade others to not accept their power and not accept the power of all of us as the ultimate arbiter.

- Fidel Castro, Hugo Chavez, Saddam Hussein, Bassar al-Assad, and Kim Jung Un have been examples of protozoa. The Russian, Iranian, and Chinese governments are examples of worms.

- It is not so much that these organisms bring about the death of the Supercivilization, as ultimately they have little power over humanity. However, they suck the life blood by draining resources that could go toward more important pursuits.

- These types of organisms are particularly dangerous during the period of a Class VIII Event. During crises, they can insert their dogma and inspire supporters to create radical divisions in the Supercivilization, thereby draining even more resources.

## Monosystem failure (as social metaphor)

When one large institution, such as the government of a nation-state, fails causing dysfunction for those directly involved (e.g. the people living in that country or other nations which interact with that country).

## Multisystem organ failure (as social metaphor)

When multiple institutions fail, such as when states go to war, resources becoming depleted and depressions occur. They become sickened organs.

## Protozoa (as social metaphor)

These are leaders who take over institutions (often failing or diseased) and create even more problems. They are public figures who think of themselves first and while they appear to be a part of society, they are not because of their underlying malevolence.

## Worms (as social metaphor)

These are groups, such as political parties, that take over failing institutions and suck the life blood out of them. They use the institutions to take from rather than to give to society.

# Bacteria

These organisms devour the Supercivilization in its weakest areas and oppose its existence. A description of them is as follows:

- These organisms are different in kind from members of the Supercivilization. They do not wish to be a part of the Supercivilization.

- They declare themselves early and are the hardiest organisms to counteract, as they are willing to die for their cause. A zero-sum game between them and the Supercivilization exists.

- They seek to destroy the current culture and want unmitigated adoption of their views by the entire Supercivilization. They are uncompromising.

- The members of these groups thrive in weakened areas of the Supercivilization such as decaying gangrenous limbs; they thrive particularly well in the Third World. They are the flesh eaters of the Supercivilization that gain a foothold in the weakened areas and spread far more effectively to the entire organism once that foothold has been established.

- Our best way of fighting these bacteria is not to try to kill them off, but rather by expending resources to decrease their ability to gain a foothold. The bacteria exist in diseased and decaying areas of the

The Supercivilization: Essential Concepts

Supercivilization and not in an organism that is healthy and has a fully functioning immune system.

- Examples include the following: Al-Qaeda, Hamas, Irish Republican Army, and Palestinian Liberation Organization.

# Viruses

These organisms are new and they exist because of three technologically based factors:

- We now have massively increased interconnectedness.

- We cannot isolate ourselves from a single world view. Viruses spread with discontent that cannot be expressed openly because of jealousy, mistrust, frustration, and envy.

- We have an overwhelming ability to intercommunicate on all levels with new technology that can cause mass destruction quickly and efficiently.

Prior to thirty years ago, open revolt was the primary means to usurp authority, and open declaration of one's intentions was necessary. September 11, 2001 was the turning point, when just nineteen people affected the lives of all 7 billion humans. A small, seemingly trivial virus of discontent was deemed possible and successfully changed the lives of all 7 billion people.

We have lost our ability to counter these groups in two important ways:

- They don't have to declare themselves to obtain capital. They can surreptitiously hijack capital in the Supercivilization to achieve their objective. Cyberwarfare is an example.

- With such a small group of terrorists, open declaration isn't necessary anymore to express discontent; it is merely an option. The timing for expressing their discontent is a huge strategic advantage for viruses against a "defenseless" Supercivilization.

Viruses have been successfully operating in the world because of the following reasons:

- Groups can be operating around us and we would be unaware of it. With the help of electronic media, these viruses can live in one area of the world and perform their nefarious work in another.

- With a virus comes the blurring of the distinction between the government and the virus. Who is wearing the white hat? The government tries to make us feel more comfortable by using any means to track social viruses down, but in so doing calls into question their pursuits and the very meaning of success. The National Security Agency and their various cyberprograms (Prism and Quantum, for example) are extremely problematic.

- The end result is that we imagine threats and our imagination runs wild. We begin to question every single activity by every single person in every single country, making us afraid of our own shadows.

- The virus causes fear and distrust of ourselves, which creates a sickened organism. When our own immune system harms us in the long run (an autoimmune disorder), we create short term victory at the expense of long term disease—much like atherosclerosis developing in a human being from repeated inflammatory insults. The effects at first seem beneficial, but the repeated misuse of our immune system is a gradually pathological event.

There is only one major solution left to combat a social virus: social cohesion through the development of a living, breathing Supercivilization. Why?

- The greater the number of people that believe in a socioeconomic system of government that seems "fair," the fewer the bacteria—and particularly fewer viruses. The bell shaped curve of human behavior will always produce pathological individuals, but the key is to make them fewer and narrow this curve distribution. We cannot and should not eliminate the tails of this curve at the expense of our long term cohesion.

- Once an individual commits a crime, it is far easier to apprehend the suspects. Sympathizers will be minimized in a strong, healthy Supercivilization, and social cohesion will lead to swift and effective arrests.

The United States had relatively little terrorism in the 20th century because of the two reasons above. At the same time our ICQ/ITQ increased, American stability and specifically our socioeconomic system generated greater disparities of wealth. We became less effective in our distribution of wealth, making extremism more likely.

Social viruses will announce themselves when the timing is best ("the perfect time") for their objective: during a Class VIII Event. This occurs during the following:

- When viruses perceive they can attack with impunity.

- When viruses create an alternative view of human society that they feel will be "credible."

- When they believe they have the capability to achieve their objective.

Our greatest fear today should be a "runaway terrorist threat" with social viruses declaring themselves simultaneously at the worst possible time. We will not have the resources to fight these viruses. And if we happen to have any resources to fight them, it will draw our resources away from other more pressing concerns, thereby creating multisystem organ failure and perhaps anarchy.

Imagine Timothy McVeigh and the resources used to apprehend him in the Oklahoma City bombing of 1995. Twenty-eight thousand interviews were conducted and a billion pieces of information were amassed for this incident alone. One might imagine the catastrophe for the United States if this number is multiplied a thousand fold with several social viruses declaring themselves at the same time in a coordinated fashion. Imagine thousands of these incidents in one year, one month, or even one day.

# Prions

This organism is now the most problematic and could lead to the end of the Supercivilization for the following reasons:

- As described in chapter 4, the biological prion is a protein-based and infectious agent (*protein* and *infection*) and unlike other life which is nucleic acid-based. Because they are not life, but merely an organic molecule that self-propagates, prions cannot be killed. They can never exist in isolation; they require organisms.

- The metaphor of the social prion is similar to a paradigm—an idea or concept held by multiple people. A social prion infects people's minds, making them unable to see different world views.

- One can destroy a prion by killing-off individuals infected with that prion. It is difficult, almost impossible, to remove a prion from someone's brain without killing them. There is no cure to dealing with people already infected with a prion, although attempts to change minds are made and are only occasionally successful. See below for possible solutions to the prion problem.

- Prions are especially dangerous in a high ICQ/ITQ environment and can infect people quickly and effectively in these environments. Positive reinforcement through the media and the "herd effect" are especially powerful tools.

- Multiple prions exist in environments that allow the fluid and free exchange of ideas and are most troublesome in liberal democratic societies. The less the exchange, the fewer the prions. If a prion is held with primacy and is unchallenged, social cohesion will improve, but at the expense of creativity, scientific advances, and problem solving.

In the past, battles between prions were insignificant, but now it is problematic. How prions functioned in each of the three eras is as follows:

- **First Biosociophysical Era:** Humans didn't know they were even infected with a prion. The only way to understand one is infected by a prion is to have a relative comparison to what people in other cultures think and feel. That was rare.

- **Second Biosociophysical Era:** Cultural hegemony was held by leaders, and during this period people understood they were infected by prions. Cultural exchange was greater but not great enough to make the prion a major agent of catastrophe that it now represents. Battles of prions were regional, not global affairs.

- **Third Biosociophysical Era:** Information exchange is rampant, leading to the battle of the prions as the *major problem* facing humanity today.

The major conundrum facing humanity today is how to safely deal with prions. There are two approaches:

- **Promote a single overarching prion (one large culture):** The problem with this approach is that one prion retards creativity and problem solving although it improves social cohesion. Those in control of this prion can potentially abuse their power (Big Brother), but create less dissension, terrorism, and war if effectively promoted. Its control must be kept in the hands of all humanity—not a minority group.

- **Promote multiple prions (limited governments with multiple cultures):** This reduces social cohesion but allows for better creativity and problem solving—especially of natural problems. Social cohesion becomes a greater problem because of the infighting amongst individuals promoting their own prion. This is an extremely dangerous issue, as promoting multiple prions leads to irrationally promoted ideas. Given our increased interconnectedness, it may be impossible to continue promoting subcivilizations.

Prions are irrational by definition; they are values we promote in individuals. However, the founding principle of a prion can be either rational or irrational. Two major types of prions exist, depending upon the prion's founding principle:

- **Rationally based prion:** This occurs when the paradigm is based on a logical principle such as mathematical laws, Einstein's theory, Darwin's theory, etc. We can and do use emotion to promote a logical principle. These are the least dangerous for society, because logic can usually counteract it if the prion is wrong.

The Supercivilization: Essential Concepts

- **Irrationally based prion:** This is based on an irrational principle that cannot be proven or disproven, such as the existence of God. This is the most dangerous type of prion, because logic cannot counteract its existence in one's mind. It is not falsifiable, so one can try and try without success to remove this prion from someone else's mind; success will elude us.

Here is the key question for our survival: How do we maintain heterogeneous creativity while maintaining a homogeneous, unifying, cohesive superculture? How do we best avoid the Big Crunch (self-annihilation of the Supercivilization) while maintaining living standards in a declining resource base? I suggest we do the following:

- Create a liberal democratic global government to promote our current cultural homogeneity and promote individual creativity and freedom. This will maximize our problem-solving potential. *Create clear, consistent, and transparent rules of conduct for all humanity that are firmly entrenched in our brains (through prion instillation) to limit government corruption and individual dysfunction. This would be a rationally based prion that all of us can create, promote, and accept as a functional, as well as logical, concept.*

- Keep the government safely in our hands (all of our hands) *before* it is forcibly imposed on us by minority interests who do not have the best interests of all of us in mind.

## The Big Crunch (sociological)

Occurs when humanity's ICQ/ITQ becomes so large that we cannot solve problems because of our physical and mental inability to comprehend a hyperdynamic environment. The crunch can be total or partial, with potentially billions of humans dead.

- Stop ignoring the social pathology that can potentially lead to our self-annihilation. We can never allow leaders like Hitler, Stalin, Assad, Khomeini, Hussein, and others who put self-interest first, to control significant portions of the Supercivilization. To ensure they never get control, we must create a liberal democratic global government.

The insidious social prion is now the cornerstone of synergistic catastrophe that I most fear. Conversely, if we are extremely careful, we can use the prion to our advantage and make our world more secure from ourselves by constructing the best prion to enhance our potential existence and eliminate a possible die-off.

## The Major Problem: Unpredictability

Unfortunately, our attempts to avoid self-annihilation are not guaranteed. We are faced with the Moser biological uncertainty principle and the notion that we can only reduce, but never eliminate, our chances of a die off. The issues are as follows:

- In spite of our attempts to mitigate our social problems, we face the ultimate problem: unpredictability. In spite of our attempts to reduce conflict and create social cohesion, we can never predict our future in a social environment. NEVER.

- In spite of our winning battles against the natural environment, as we try to understand our social world, we learn that it is less controllable. We are going backward and not forward in our ability to predict and control our future for our benefit. Our science is breaking down.

- As smaller and smaller human-induced events make a larger and larger impact on our world, we are destined to live with unpredictability.

- Creating an aura of trust will allow the social world some ability to manage conflict and unpredictability. It is our only hope. The civilized state is the key to our survival and the prion will be its tool for our survival. Steven Pinker writes, "Many criminologists believe that the source of the state's pacifying effect isn't just its brute coercive power but the trust it commands among the populace."

Chapter 10

# Synergistic Catastrophe

"Politics must continue; war cannot. That is not to say that the role of the warrior is over. The world community needs, more than it has ever done, skilful and disciplined warriors who are ready to put themselves at the service of its authority. Such warriors must properly be seen as the protectors of civilisation, not its enemies."

—*John Keegan, author of* A History of Warfare

# Resonant Social Pathology

Resonant social pathology—a uniform emotive response to an event that is transmitted throughout society—is now the greatest problem facing the Supercivilization. It can be further explained as follows:

- We can use a wave model to explain resonant social pathology: Waves blown onto the ocean shore occur because wind energy hits the waves, causing more accumulated energy and creating eddies that make deeper troughs and larger crests. The waves grow larger because the atmosphere's energy is blowing in one direction. If the atmosphere's energy wasn't moving in one direction, wind would not occur and waves would not form. Like the waves on an ocean shore, waves of social pathology can flourish in an interconnected world, as one event can quickly cause others to respond, causing others to respond to those responses.

- Why does most pathology remain benign (tolerable to the Supercivilization)? Is it luck? It is because this pathology is not coordinated and does not resonate to conspire and create one massive catastrophic event at the same time. The pathology was random in the past, but now it has the potential to produce coordinated effects.

- For the Swiss-cheese thinker, resonance makes little sense, but for the planetary-formation thinker, it makes perfect sense. Luck or chance is based on random interactions. Resonant interaction is based upon uniform, spontaneous reactions. Suddenly no event or human activity is completely isolated.

- The herd effect is the cornerstone of resonant social pathology. We look to others to help us determine our reactions to events. Whether reading the editorial of a newspaper during a political crisis, viewing neighbors' reactions during an earthquake, or looking at other drivers in heavy traffic and their reactions to an accident, we respond to crises by seeing the response of others around us.

- Because of our interconnectedness, we can get immediate feedback from others, which can cause waves of resonant motion that distribute energy or emotional reaction throughout the Supercivilization quite rapidly.

# A World of Tipping Points

As Malcolm Gladwell has stated, the world of tipping points is upon us. But why? Why now?

- In the past, waves of information were slow, indistinct, and required multiple relays. These waves usually died because of the poor delivery of the transmitted message. Also, the individuals receiving the messages were less likely to identify with the people transmitting them. Because there were several interpretations by different media residing in different cultures, these emotive waves generated little capacity to resonate throughout humanity.

- Today, we view our world as an homogenizing, single culture. We now identify with others and readily accept the more directed interpretation being transmitted from single primary sources. We trust our sources and are more accepting of facts, while at the same time we empathize with the victims of these events.

- Malcolm Gladwell points out the following: "We are all at heart, gradualists, our expectations set by the gradual passage of time. But the world of the Tipping Point is a place where the unexpected becomes expected, where radical change is more than a possibility. It is—contrary to all our expectations—a certainty."

# Call the Coroner: The 20th Century Nation-State Is Dead

The concept of the nation-state is obsolete. Here is why:

- Our culture has several dimensions: geographical, institutional, ideological, and material, among the many. Politics is just one dimension of our culture which has not progressed as quickly as the other dimensions.

- The Gladwellian tipping point of the nation-state's demise has already occurred. It occurred around the year 2000. As the Internet was taking hold, the nation-state was officially pronounced dead with a second event—September 11. The nation-state is obsolete, as we now reside in nations but are really a Supercivilization. It is not clear where one culture ends and another begins. Our commitments no longer put the nation-state supremely ahead of other institutions. Our loyalties are divided and include:

  » **Corporate loyalty:** Both as consumers and employees, people often feel more loyalty to corporations than nations. People assign loyalty to products like Nike, McDonalds, Boeing, Sony, and Siemens, which have no clearly defined national base. Of the one hundred largest economies, 51 are corporate in nature. Corporate advertising ($100 billion annually) outpaces nation-state propaganda. How can governments compete with 20,000 30-second commercials the average child sees annually (two million by the age of 65 years)?

» **Family loyalty:** Members of the same family often live in different regions of the world regardless of national boundaries.

» **Political ideological loyalty:** Many who believe in right wing agendas (less government) and left wing agendas (more government) span the globe and are major points in the platforms of political parties in nearly all the world's countries.

» **Religious loyalty:** Whether a Christian, Muslim, Jew or a member of other organized religions, individuals find common bonding in religious loyalty regardless of the nation-state.

• Trust is the key to successful market capitalization and economic growth. To have both, you need to have minimal government corruption. With so many corrupt governments today, we cannot maximize the economic growth until all the rules are well defined and the playing field is level for all people in the world. Comments by leading economists are as follows:

» Partha Gupta writes about a recent study, "Not surprisingly, the data also reveal that trust and government corruption moved together, but in opposite directions. The two variables were negatively (and significantly) correlated."

» Martin Wolfe, noted economic journalist, writes, "The flow of *reliable* information and *trust* is the life-blood of markets."

» Harvard economist James Wilson argues, "Trust must exist in a society for it to be a capitalist society because people who do not trust their neighbors, do not trust other groups, ... cannot trade with them; and, unable to trade with them, capitalism remains at the level of a bazaar economy."

# Resonant Waves of Social Pathology

Currently, the problem with pathology isn't the pathological event itself; it is the reaction to the pathology that is the most troublesome.

- The subjective experience of the Supercivilization, not the objective experience is what is so damaging.

- The *perception* of the reality, not reality itself, will herald our collective demise.

- The events that cause waves are getting smaller, yet the waves are getting larger and are affecting more people in the Supercivilization.

- Smaller pathological events attract more media attention throughout the world via the same reports, causing quick amplification of this event; the event appears to be more significant than it really is.

- WikiLeaks, a drop of 600 points in the stock market from a single broker error in May 2010, and the self-immolation of a Tunisian vendor are just three examples of these relatively minute pathological events that create massive waves of resonant pathology.

- Even more critical, we understand the tremendous waves we can cause, and we are now more likely to use them to influence the Supercivilization for our own benefit especially when we are desperate.

# Civilization as Lakes Model: The Single Event

To describe a single pathological event's effect on the rest of humanity, I utilize the civilization-as-lakes model (Figure 10.1A to D).

- Like lakes with rippling waves from a disturbance (such as a pebble thrown into a pond), so too are these waves of social pathology.

- The larger the body of water, the more likely the waves will propagate to more people.

- Isolated lakes or civilizations are not affected by the social pathology that exists in other lakes.

- Third World countries remain the most vulnerable to the natural problem; the First World with all its media and penetration into the general public are far more vulnerable to social pathology; hence the social problem.

- Homogenization of culture also propagates these waves, because we identify with more people from more distant geographical areas than ever before.

  » Although there are 6500 languages on Earth, over half are spoken by fewer than 10,000 people.

  » The Internet is the universal language. Individuals using the same computer programs can now understand one single programming language.

  » Eighty percent of the world's electronic information is stored in English.

  » Virtually all diplomats in all countries speak English, and one quarter of all people on Earth speak some English. Never before has this world become so culturally homogeneous.

  » Sense of self in other countries has even become Westernized; we are unifying our perception, causation, and treatment patterns of psychiatric illness. There are sharp rises of anorexia in Hong Kong, PTSD in Sri Lanka, schizophrenia in Zanzibar, and mega-marketing of depression in Japan.

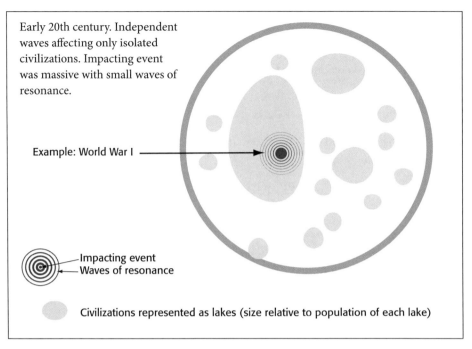

Early 20th century. Independent waves affecting only isolated civilizations. Impacting event was massive with small waves of resonance.

Example: World War I

Impacting event
Waves of resonance

Civilizations represented as lakes (size relative to population of each lake)

FIGURE 10.1 A   A Model For the Development of Social Pathology as Waves of Resonance: Civilizations as Lakes

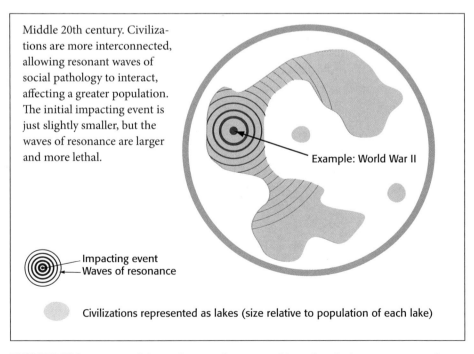

Middle 20th century. Civilizations are more interconnected, allowing resonant waves of social pathology to interact, affecting a greater population. The initial impacting event is just slightly smaller, but the waves of resonance are larger and more lethal.

Example: World War II

Impacting event
Waves of resonance

Civilizations represented as lakes (size relative to population of each lake)

FIGURE 10.1 B   A Model For the Development of Social Pathology as Waves of Resonance: Civilizations as Lakes

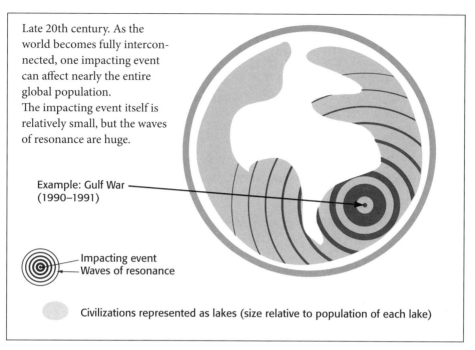

**FIGURE 10.1 C** A Model For the Development of Social Pathology as Waves of Resonance: Civilizations as Lakes

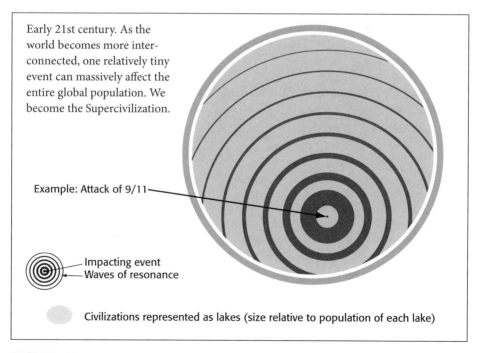

**FIGURE 10.1 D** A Model For the Development of Social Pathology as Waves of Resonance: Civilizations as Lakes

# Multiple Waves: How They Are Coordinated Matters

It is not necessarily the type of event or even the size of the event that matters. The Supercivilization will have pathology, but it is how this pathology is coordinated that matters (Figure 10.2 A to D).

- The timing of the pathology is most critical. Multiple waves timed perfectly are far more damaging than random pathology that is tragic, yet senseless, because the latter cannot move people emotionally in the same direction as effectively.

- A sensationalistic media looking for stories to write is also necessary.

- Lately, media have laid off staff, making the general public more subject to manipulation by others and their pathological events.

  » Thirty of the fifty largest US newspapers are losing money.

  » Revenues for newspapers are off 40 percent from 2006.

  » Specialized expert reporters are fewer in number. For example, 150 newspapers had a science section just two decades ago; today fewer than 20 do.

  » Even the *New York Times* recently laid off 100 specialized reporters.

- With the loss of the guardians of accurate information and the rise of the Internet comes easy manipulation of the news by vested interests, including terrorists.

- Desperate newspapers and broadcast networks seeking stories to boost their circulation and their ratings are now primed to assist the terrorists in their promotion of their pathology.

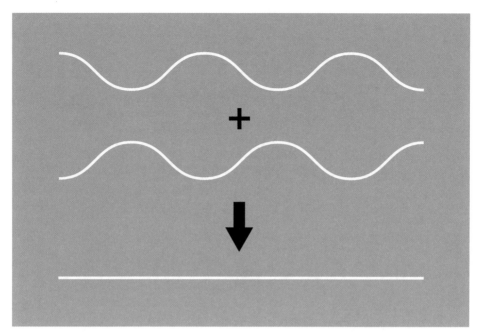

**FIGURE 10.2 A**  Interaction Between Multiple Pathological Social Waves
*With canceling waves of resonant social pathology, the result is minimal social impact.*

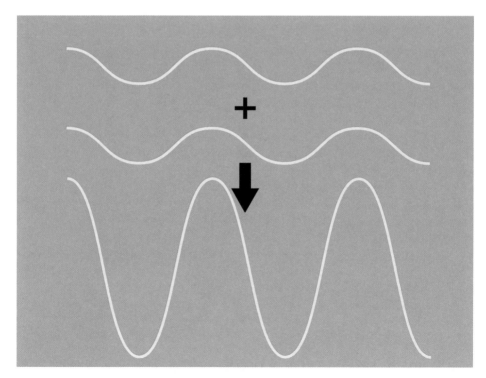

**FIGURE 10.2 B**  Interaction Between Multiple Pathological Social Waves
*With additive waves of resonant social pathology, the result is a potentially huge impact.*

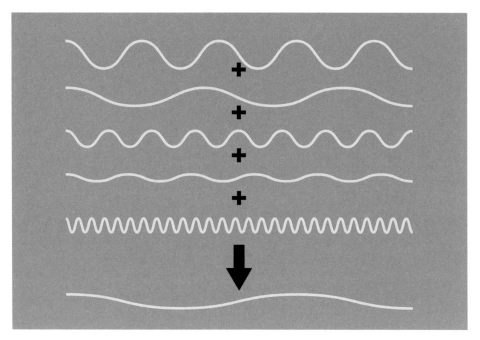

**FIGURE 10.2 C**  Interaction Between Multiple Pathological Social Waves
*With random waves of resonant social pathology, the result has a usually canceling, minimal impact.*

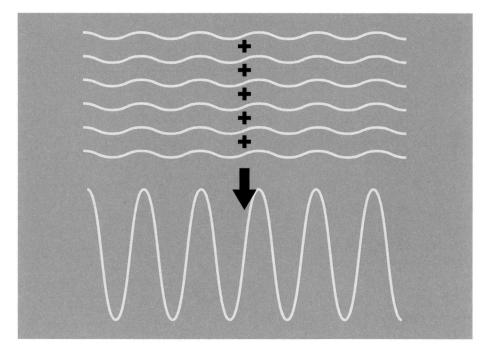

**FIGURE 10.2 D**  Interaction Between Multiple Pathological Social Waves
*Synchronized waves of social pathology coordinated through communication devices (for example, cell phones) can lead to potentially catastrophic events.*

# Civilization as Lakes Model: The Synergistic Event

The synergistic event is now possible. Small events, timed simultaneously, will create massive waves of destruction (Figure 10.3 A to D). It is these events we need to fear the most, not the natural pathology that vested interests love to point to as the problem.

- The world is now one large lake, metaphorically speaking.

- Pathology can produce additive, subtractive, or precisely cancelling waves.

- Most of the time, random pathology produces waves that are self-cancelling, producing little resonance in the minds of individuals. No massive waves are produced; there is little, if any net effect on the Supercivilization. Random crime is drowned out in our minds because it always happens without meaningful danger to most of us.

- In a planetary-formation world, pathology can be coordinated and *enhance* the chances that other pathology will occur. In a Swiss-cheese world, pathology does not influence other pathology, as each pathological event is isolated; precise timing is impossible.

- When individuals can see the possibility that pathology is successful, it will encourage others to engage in other pathological behavior or perform acts that react to that pathology; it may also inspire others to perform acts that supplement the original pathology.

- Terrorists may specifically perform all pathological acts in unison to overwhelm authorities in their capability to apprehend them.

- Terrorists may also use other types of natural pathology (earthquake, tsunami, disease outbreaks, etc) and social pathology (war, economic meltdowns, and institutional abuse) to perform their pathological acts in order to gain leverage against a weakened Supercivilization.

- The synergistic moment can occur when a tsunami of natural and social events causes massive waves that occur simultaneously, making our world a gigantic negative feedback system. This could become a Class VIII Event.

- As our ICQ/ITQ increase, resources decline, disparity in wealth grows, and technology improves, our world will become more susceptible to a Class VIII Event.

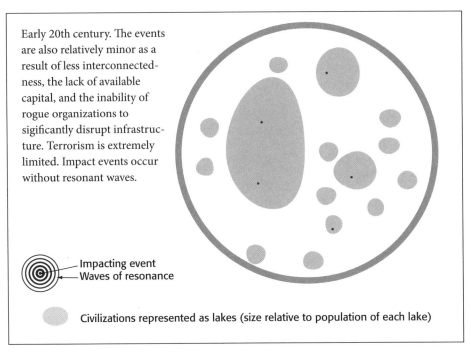

Early 20th century. The events are also relatively minor as a result of less interconnectedness, the lack of available capital, and the inability of rogue organizations to significantly disrupt infrastructure. Terrorism is extremely limited. Impact events occur without resonant waves.

Impacting event
Waves of resonance

Civilizations represented as lakes (size relative to population of each lake)

**FIGURE 10.3 A**  The Civilizations as Lakes Model Demonstrating the Potential for Acts of Terrorism for Sociologically Modern Humans

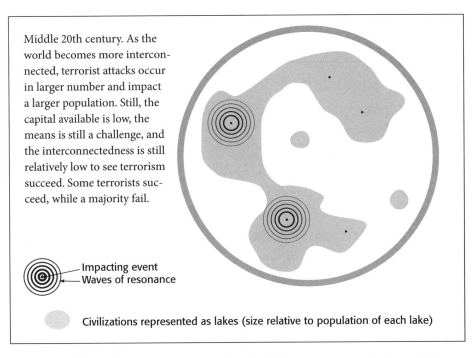

Middle 20th century. As the world becomes more interconnected, terrorist attacks occur in larger number and impact a larger population. Still, the capital available is low, the means is still a challenge, and the interconnectedness is still relatively low to see terrorism succeed. Some terrorists succeed, while a majority fail.

Impacting event
Waves of resonance

Civilizations represented as lakes (size relative to population of each lake)

**FIGURE 10.3 B**  The Civilizations as Lakes Model Demonstrating the Potential for Acts of Terrorism for Sociologically Modern Humans

The Supercivilization: Essential Concepts

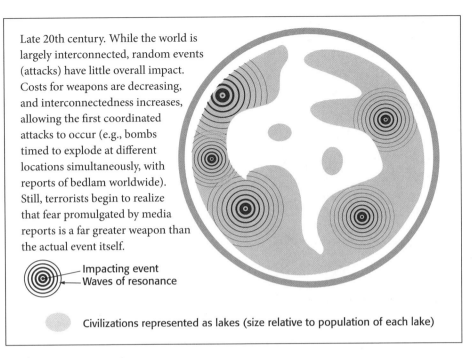

Late 20th century. While the world is largely interconnected, random events (attacks) have little overall impact. Costs for weapons are decreasing, and interconnectedness increases, allowing the first coordinated attacks to occur (e.g., bombs timed to explode at different locations simultaneously, with reports of bedlam worldwide). Still, terrorists begin to realize that fear promulgated by media reports is a far greater weapon than the actual event itself.

Impacting event
Waves of resonance

Civilizations represented as lakes (size relative to population of each lake)

**FIGURE 10.3 C** The Civilizations as Lakes Model Demonstrating the Potential for Acts of Terrorism for Sociologically Modern Humans

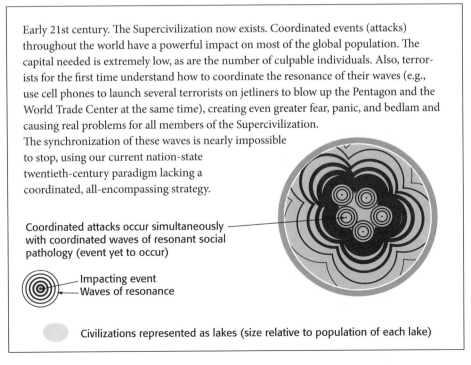

Early 21st century. The Supercivilization now exists. Coordinated events (attacks) throughout the world have a powerful impact on most of the global population. The capital needed is extremely low, as are the number of culpable individuals. Also, terrorists for the first time understand how to coordinate the resonance of their waves (e.g., use cell phones to launch several terrorists on jetliners to blow up the Pentagon and the World Trade Center at the same time), creating even greater fear, panic, and bedlam and causing real problems for all members of the Supercivilization. The synchronization of these waves is nearly impossible to stop, using our current nation-state twentieth-century paradigm lacking a coordinated, all-encompassing strategy.

Coordinated attacks occur simultaneously with coordinated waves of resonant social pathology (event yet to occur)

Impacting event
Waves of resonance

Civilizations represented as lakes (size relative to population of each lake)

**FIGURE 10.3 D** The Civilizations as Lakes Model Demonstrating the Potential for Acts of Terrorism for Sociologically Modern Humans

## Socioplacebo-like effect

Much like outcomes of a disease where processes in the human body are influenced by expectations for success or failure by the human nervous system (we are sick if we think we are sick by definition of the disease state), so too are social conditions impacted by the collective consciousness of the Supercivilization. Our success at solving pathology of the Supercivilization depends on our ability to control our collective consciousness and exploit our socioplacebo-like effect for social problems. Our collective mental state as a civilization is what we think it is: no more and no less. The collective consciousness of society is a manifestation of our will to cohesively integrate in order to problem solve. By doing so, we make the socioplacebo-like effect a positive, controllable reality. If we don't control our collective consciousness, we will succumb to a reality controlled by independent sub-entities taking advantage of the socioplacebo- like effect.

# The Role of the Prion in Synergy

We can protect against social pathology if we realize this pathology has the potential to create massive resonance. We have not taken the steps to reduce this pathology yet. Why?

- Our biggest problem is that we harbor an obsolete prion that promotes the nation-state and a Swiss-cheese world that operates on a 20th century level of technology.

- Because a Class VIII synergistic event has never occurred in civilized humans, we ignore its possibility. A moon landing never occurred before 1969, but would one call the landing on the moon in 1960 an impossible event merely because it had never happened in human existence?

- We must work to create a prion that will comfortably eliminate the real possibility of a Class VIII Event. If we don't, we will have a problematic prion instilled in our minds.

- We must eliminate an illusion of stability and focus on preventing a Class VIII Event that could happen in our lifetimes.

# Succumbing to the Socioplacebo-like Effect

The goal in avoiding these resonant social pathological events is to avoid creating dependence upon authority figures. An egalitarian society is most desirable. Just as the placebo effect relates to medication use in the clinical setting, the socioplacebo-like effect relates to the social setting of the Supercivilization, as does its command and control over our psyche.

- Like the placebo effect in medicine, the socioplacebo-like effect is the manipulation of our world views by authority figures who convince us we are sick, so we seek *their* solutions that benefit them and not necessarily us.

- An even greater threat to us isn't the terrorist; it is our imagination. When we imagine pathology, we create nonsensical solutions that may produce more harm than good.

- We can allow others to convince us we are sick, so they will prescribe a beneficial therapy. The problem is that if we allow minority interests to convince us we need their prescription to solve our problems, we succumb to the socioplacebo-like effect.

- The healthier and more egalitarian our Supercivilization is, the less likely we are to be susceptible to this effect and less likely to be manipulated. Powerful minority interests will have less control over the institutions, especially the state, that control the agenda.

The major goal should be to instill in all of us a safe, more effective prion that will promote egalitarianism and allow us to control our emotions. An institution is required that allows us to safely promote our common goals and resolve our disagreements in a binding fashion.

# III. Solutions for the Supercivilization's Sustenance

"The success of the United States will be measured by its ability to lift the entire world to its standard of living; its failure will be to remain as the most dominant power, mired in its own success."

—John Moser

# Chapter 11

# Global Realization

"If mankind could so quickly destroy the majority of the world's big game with a primitive Stone Age technology, what hope have the world's creatures in the face of our far more advanced technology?"

—*Peter Ward, author of* The End of Evolution

# Critical Need for Leadership

Today's Supercivilization is most critically lacking in leadership. It isn't our declining resource base, our interconnectedness, or our disparities in wealth that are the primary threat. It is the lack of leadership that greatly magnifies these problems and makes them irresolvable. Without strong leadership, we are a dying patient. Treating the patient requires the following:

- To coordinate ideas and interventions, we must have one voice—one lead trauma surgeon or one symphony conductor.

- Teams must be experienced and know how their subject matter must be coordinated so that inefficiencies and duplications do not occur. Unwanted gibberish and talk in the trauma room only makes for poor outcomes and distracts us from our mission.

- It isn't the closest hospital to a life-threatening trauma that makes the difference; it is the nearest trauma center that puts all the different pieces together in a coordinated fashion that is practiced over and over. If all the members of a team are not present and all the necessary duties are not practiced in unison, a misadventure could occur that will kill the patient.

# Time Is Our Enemy

When we are held accountable for our actions or inactions, progress is made. Sometimes the price is precious life or merely an inconvenience for many. In all cases time is our enemy and procrastination is falsely promoted as the ideal solution.

- Watershed moments are necessary for our survival and can serve to promote unity. These moments usually inspire leadership and are then followed by assertive action. The problem is that they are responses to mounting problems that were preceded by weak leadership:

  » Abraham Flexner's report on medical education in 1910 inspired the growth of more closely scrutinized training of doctors.

  » President Franklin Roosevelt's "Day of Infamy" speech in 1941 led to a resurgent military challenge against the Axis in World War II.

  » President John F. Kennedy's moon landing speech in 1961 ended with Neil Armstrong's thunderous step in 1969.

  » Martin Luther King's "I Have a Dream Speech" in 1963 promoted integration and enlightened so many about the respect humans should give one another.

- » The Surgeon General's landmark report on smoking in 1964 led to the decline of cigarette sales after years of growth.

- » President Ronald Reagan's speech on the Berlin Wall helped motivate the Soviet bloc to remove barriers that kept two polarized worlds separated by ideology.

- » Al Gore's Inconvenient Truth and the 2007 IPCC report could act to turn our careless carbon emissions around, but we have yet to see that happen definitively.

- Raising capital to promote global solutions without a direct profit motive is difficult if not impossible. Jeffrey Sachs states, "Raising capital for global public goods is hard enough; raising funds for scientific research and technology development is harder still when targets of the research are for global needs, not national economic advantage or private profits."

- Our fight-or-flight mechanism makes our survival so razor thin: if we think we will survive, we will not; if we think we will not survive, we will. The stress can produce two possibilities:

- » If we use our adrenaline surge correctly and efficiently channel it, we will be immensely successful.

- » If we haphazardly allow our adrenaline surge to overcome us, we will oversee a Class VIII Event.

- Deadlines and accountability for every human being are the key ways to channel and promote necessary adrenaline surges to promote effective social change.

# The Rise of Hitler in a Rudderless World

The greatest fear of poor leadership is the development of a surrogate leader who provides extremist, even dangerous views, as viable alternatives to a rudderless world. Hitler was one such leader who was responsible for a major die-off in the first half of the twentieth century.

- Post-World War I was a time in which the world had no leadership and was intent on punishing Germany for its failures of World War I. As a result, the German economy—and then the world economy—hit a horrific low that stirred intense emotions of hatred, making extremism more likely.

- Poor leadership and accountability will create massive ambivalence. Leaders who have no ethics and no accountability will take advantage of an ambivalent, yet volatile world.

- Adolf Hitler took advantage of a world without leadership by bringing humanity to the brink of self-annihilation in the 1930s and 1940s. Hitler was the only person with a clear plan, and though he was a lunatic, he took advantage of the poor leadership around him to savagely and brutally attack those areas of the world that lacked the same leadership.

In spite of overwhelming evidence, President Roosevelt, Prime Minister Neville Chamberlain, and Premier Edouard Daladier ignored Hitler's ultimatums for several years. Little could be done until the threat was so dire that only a last ditch response to his plans was implemented. At post-Nuremburg trials, German generals were astonished at how Britain and France ignored Hitler's ultimatums and had such a weak response to his militaristic and bellicose activities.

- Today, we are facing a world without strong leadership and accountability. Our opposition is ourselves and not Hitler. Those who only put self-interest ahead of the Supercivilization are going to create a catastrophe because they don't realize how much harm they are doing.

- Currently, accountability is lacking in many areas of the world. The United Nations was built to respect and even promote the supreme sovereignty of each nation even when those nations were corrupt. It has failed because corrupt governments are just as dangerous as the terrorists they may harbor. In the 20th century, the internal politics of each country rarely affected surrounding countries; today, the effects can be massive.

- Project Alliance is the creation of a global government and is the first step toward stronger leadership and accountability of every human being. Project Alliance is a proposed ten-year period in which a transition will take place from nation-states to global government. It is a full commitment by all 196 countries to create a global government in which accountability of all humans is placed squarely in the hands of all of us.

# Linus Pauling: Our Potential Waterloo

Our Supercivilization is in need of more than just strong leadership. We are in need of critical problem-solving approaches that require more than just a scientific approach. While we must continue carefully applying the scientific method to social and biological science, its application is limited by reflexivity and the ethics of dealing with biological organisms. Linus Pauling's Waterloo is a lesson:

- Linus Pauling was a brilliant scientist who won two Nobel prizes in two separate fields.

- He wrote about Vitamin C and its effects on the common cold. He advocated taking 1000 mg of Vitamin C daily to help ward off colds.

- His theories were ultimately proven, at best, to be inconclusive and most doctors would say he was simply wrong.

- Pauling was more interested in proving he was right than he was in finding the truth. That is a problem in the social and biological sciences, as vested interests frequently interfere with purely objective research.

- He quickly found that the application of scientific concepts used in the physical world were not necessarily applicable to the biological world.

- His theories were promoted merely because of his distinguished background and not as a result of good science. Others believed his conclusions and many profits were made by third parties because of reputation, not evidence.

Our application of science to the social and biological world is proving to be disastrous and is much more difficult than we thought imaginable. Our scientific community has been so smug, like Pauling, in its abilities to conquer the physical world, that our scientific methodology is breaking down in its generalized applications. Our experiences in dealing with problems in the physical world are much easier to resolve than the social or biological world.

# Competition Versus Cooperation

Is the Supercivilization better served through competition or cooperation? Both are necessary to promote our existence, but regulated competition is the key factor to our success as a species in high ICQ/ITQ environments. To promote this type of success, voluntary development of a global government is necessary. It needs to be produced from within by all of us and not by minority interests for the following reasons:

- The biggest fear of a global government is Big Brother. This is unfounded, especially if we create it before it is imposed upon us involuntarily. By choosing our government in a carefully controlled fashion with critical protections of liberties, we can avoid a major pitfall, such as a die-off because of a Class VIII Event followed by an eventual installation of a government that is corrupt and without liberal democratic protections.

- If we carefully create accountability of all humans through a global government that we ourselves select, operate, and control, we can eliminate chance and dangerous uncertainty. I fear it is only a matter of time before a dangerous prion will either be imposed on us by rogue nations or lead to a catastrophic die-off that will occur from our defense against such a rogue leader.

- Our interconnectedness makes rogue terrorists and rogue leaders far more likely to impose their will on the entire Supercivilization. We can no longer afford to overlook the corruption occurring in nations any longer. Currently, national sovereignty is a supreme right. The impenetrable nature of the nation-state currently encourages rogue state behavior that can migrate to other nations and across the globe quickly. Two examples of this international indifference to human rights include the following:

  » Idi Amin's Uganda was appointed to the United Nations Council on Human Rights from 1971-1979 in spite of 100,000 to 300,000 government sponsored murders.

  » More recently the 47 nation Council on Human Rights was about to release a report praising Muammar el-Qaddafi for his human rights record in spite of his bloodthirsty murders of his own people. It was only withheld when he started a bloodbath during his civil war.

- All nation-states were formed by happenstance, quirks of history, war, and even corruption. These chance events represent inequalities that should be corrected through a careful blueprint that makes more sense.

- There is a natural predilection for nation-states to compete because of these quirks, and when there is no regulator to monitor such competition, corruption and disagreements abound. Most governments of the past existed in spite of, rather than because of, themselves.

- Governments that have the most accountability and appear to have the most integrity are the ones that will survive. Because nation-state formation was ad hoc, the nations that offered its citizens the greatest standards of living were primarily the ones to survive.

- Better leadership will also mean more equality. Roger Wilkinson and Kate Pickett studied nine variables and found that those countries with the most equitable incomes had the least dysfunction and were the healthiest societies. The countries with the most equitable incomes had the following nine characteristics:

  » Highest level of trust

  » Least mental illness (including drug and alcohol addiction)

  » Highest life expectancy and lowest infant mortality

  » Lowest obesity rates

  » Best children's educational performance

  » Lowest number of teenage births

  » Fewest homicides

  » Lowest imprisonment rates

  » Most social mobility

- Most important, Wilkinson and Pickett found it was not the type of socio-economic system, overall wealth of a society, or type of social paradigms that determined dysfunction; it was the amount of equality.

- Wilkinson and Pickett also showed it was not whether taxation or narrowed salary ranges occurred, but merely the amount of equality. For example, Japan, with narrowed salary ranges or Sweden. with high taxation, promoted the same amount of success.

- Wilkinson and Pickett probably would be aghast at the overall equality (or inequality) in the entire Supercivilization and how great the disparities are. Before the Supercivilization, these disparities didn't matter, but with the increased interconnectedness, they are critical to resolve.

- Totally free markets without regulation (much like the Supercivilization today) have led to huge disparities in wealth, making the Supercivilization highly dysfunctional.

- The idea that wealth will magically trickle down to the working class is wrong. The facts of the last one hundred years do not bear this out.

Whether in the marketplace, court of law, or the legislature, the power of those with money can skew the playing field.

- Today in the United States, the wealthiest 1 percent earn 23 percent of the country's household income. The last time this figure was this high was just before the Great Depression (24 percent). The period of maximal growth for this country between 1945–1971 saw this same 1 percent earning just 9–12 percent of the household income.

- The pay of CEOs of major United States corporations went from 42 times the average worker's pay in 1980 (before deregulation) to 531 times in 2000, when deregulation was in full effect.

- Regulated competition by an authority such as a global government must occur to keep the wealthy from skewing the playing field so far to their advantage that social conditions become too dysfunctional. Without a government to regulate competition not just between individuals, but also (and more importantly) between nation-states, this dysfunction will prove catastrophic.

## Sports as a Metaphor for the Supercivilization

Today, competitive sports serve as an ideal model for studying controlled competition. We now can view three professional leagues and see one that is thriving, one languishing, and one in decline.

- Competitive sports is an estimated $213 billion industry in the United States. It is twice the size of the auto industry and seven times the size of the movie industry.

- Professional sports leagues are transparent and are closely scrutinized by the media, which allows us to see how cooperation can work.

- Professional team sports in particular reflect society's values and norms.

- Although "the toy box of human civilization" as Harry Edwards, sports sociologist, is fond of saying, team sports can give us important insight as to how cooperation can produce benefits for all participants.

- The three most popular United States' sports leagues show how cooperation (or lack thereof) can lead to success:
  » National Football League: a league in ascension
  » National Basketball Association: a league that is languishing
  » Major League Baseball: a league in decline

The current state of these three leagues is described below.

## National Football League: Thriving and Proactive

Here is a summary of the NFL and why, in spite of its recent domestic violence issues, it is in ascension:

- The NFL enjoys high television ratings (eight of the top ten Nielson-rated programs in 2010). Recently, a thirty-second commercial during the Super Bowl sold for $3.5 million.

- The NFL has a great return on revenues ($1.07 billion on $9 billion in revenues).

- Most games are sold out and 147 million Americans recently tuned into all or part of the Super Bowl, roughly half of all Americans.

- Generally this is the favorite sport of fans. The Harris poll in 2008 reflected the following facts:

  » Thirty percent of fans chose NFL football as their favorite professional sport, up from 24 percent in 1985 (a 25 percent increase).

  » Four percent chose NBA basketball, which is down from 6 percent in 1985 (a 33 percent decrease).

  » Fifteen percent chose Major League Baseball, which is down from 23 percent in 1985 (a 35 percent decrease).

- All 32 teams' revenues are shared equally and place strict caps on spending.

- The highest valued franchise (Dallas Cowboys $1.65 billion) in 2009 was roughly double the least valued franchise (Oakland Raiders $787 million), a ratio of 2.1:1.

- The highest average team salary was $1.18 million versus a low of $537,000 in 2009 or a 2:1 ratio.

- Team salaries are fluid and can change dramatically from year to year and team to team.

- The NFL discourages onfield celebrations and all teams are structured on putting the team ahead of the individual. Individual statistics are of secondary importance to winning.

- The NFL is strictly a team sport whereby all plays rely on the complete success of all the players performing at their optimum without error. The coach is the "choreographer" who designs the plays to match the strengths and weaknesses of his players.

- Most important, no team is a clear winner every year. Winners are unpredictable and based upon hard work, perseverance, dedication, and team effort. In the past 45 Super Bowls, no team has won more than six championships (13 percent), with 18 of the 32 teams (56 percent) having won the Super Bowl at least once.

- The league office clearly sets the agenda, promotes the entire league, and does not play favorites. Teams do not tell the commissioner what to do; the commissioner uses his powers as collectively voted on by all owners with equal weight. He is given the centralized authority with clearly defined functions and independent authority to monitor and even moderate team competition.

## National Basketball Association: Languishing

The National Basketball Association is a league with mixed success.

- Only five players are on the court, leading to more individualism and allowing one player to make a huge impact on one team compared to football and basketball.

- The NBA had $4.1 billion in revenues in the 2010–11 season, which is less than half of NFL revenues. The NBA's operating income was only $183 million (less than one-fifth the NFL).

- Twenty-two of the league's 30 teams lost money (a total of $300 million).

- Shared revenue is slight (increased in 2008 from $30 million to $49 million), which is 12 percent of total revenue.

- Beginning in the 1980s the NBA promoted the "player," such as Michael Jordan, Larry Bird, Earvin "Magic" Johnson, and others.

- Since 1980 when the "player" concept was first introduced, just 9 of 30 teams have won championships. The Los Angeles Lakers have won 9 times (31 percent). Just six teams accounted for 91 percent of the last 32 championships. Every year a team (especially its fans) can pretty much predict where it will finish in the league standings before the season begins.

- Players realize that teams need them more than they need teams, so owners will often side with disgruntled players rather than the coaches or other team members during a dispute.

- The salary cap is "soft" because it contains several exceptions which give huge advantages to the wealthiest owners in the wealthiest cities.

- Team salaries ranged from a high of $91 million (Los Angeles Lakers) to a low of $29 million (Denver Nuggets) which is a ratio of 3.1:1.

- Team values are far less than the NFL and range from a high of $607 million (Los Angeles Lakers) to a low of $254 million (Milwaukee Bucks), a ratio of 2.4:1.

- Integrity has also come into question with a recent "fixing" scandal by an NBA referee, an assault of a coach by a player, reports of gunplay during a game, and a brawl that emptied the stands involving spectators, players, and coaches.

- Nielson ratings have dropped from an all-time high of 18.5 for the final game of the 1996–97 championship series to an all-time low of 6.2 of the 2006–07 final championship game. Networks have virtually stopped showing regular season games.

- Most important, players and owners in the NBA believe the league needs them more than then they need the league, which produces infighting, greed, and major dysfunction.

## Major League Baseball: Declining and Reactive

Baseball is clearly the most dysfunctional sport.

- Participation by players is limited at any given time. Most players are standing around watching the game and looking at a duel between a pitcher and a batter.

- Individual statistics are paramount to success in baseball and winning is somewhat secondary, given that few teams with low paying payrolls stand any chance of winning the World Series. Player contracts directly reflect the player statistics and not team success.

- There is no firm salary cap, but recently 6 percent ($433 million) was shared using a complex formula based on a competitive balance tax.

- Ticket prices have soared from $2.25 in 1964 to $26.79 in 2009 to support player salaries.

- While attendance is stable, television revenues are down. Only $340 million in television revenues were received compared to $2.2 billion for the NFL.

- Major League Baseball has $7.2 billion in revenues, but operating income is only $469 million, less than half of football.

- MLB has had serious losses of potential revenue as it has gone from America's favorite sport to a seriously flawed enterprise. Given the numbers of games, revenues of $10 to 20 billion could be expected if baseball (players, coaches, management, and league offices) had put the sport ahead of the individual.

- In 2000, a blue ribbon panel chaired by Paul Volcker, former chairman of the Federal Reserve, even argued that disparities in revenues was ruining the sport. In the 1990s no team in the bottom half of total expenditures on salaries won a single post-season game. Their suggestions fell mainly on deaf ears, as revenue sharing has remained a mere pittance.

- Local television rights for the New York Yankees was $67 million—nearly five times the average television rights of the 13 smallest markets ($13.5 million).

- The New York Yankees recently signed three free agents for $423 million which was more than the value of 16 other teams. That same year the 29 other teams combined spent a total of $297 million on free agents.

- The Yankees were recently valued five times as much ($1.6 billion) as the Florida Marlins ($317 million).

- The payroll of the Yankees in 2011 was $203 million compared to $36 million for the Kansas City Royals.

- Individual achievements are often thrust ahead of even World Series champions. Few remember who won the World Series in 2007 (Boston Red Sox), but most would remember Barry Bonds' quest for 756 career home runs.

- Steroid testing has been a major problem with an initial estimate of 5 to 7 percent of players using performance-enhancing drugs. After Barry Bonds, Roger Clemens, and Alex Rodriguez have all been substantially found to have used performance-enhancing drugs, that low figure is highly suspect.

- To no one's surprise, the New York Yankees have won 27 of the 107 World Series or 25 percent. The St. Louis Cardinals have won the second most at 11 percent.

- There is only one superpower and that superpower dictates to the league and not vice versa: The New York Yankees. There is little oversight by the league and the real power is held by the large market teams, especially the New York Yankees.

- Until very recently (mainly because of public outcry), performance-enhancing drugs, instant replay, and league disparities are three issues the league is reactively trying to deal with, but has been largely unsuccessful at addressing. Everyone attending accepts the limitations. The catch word "tradition" is bandied about as good public relations.

The New York Yankees in baseball and the United States in the Supercivilization are the superpowers that believe their interests are being preserved when in reality they are both sinking rapidly in a quicksand of individualism. They both respond to problems only when forced to and use their power to preserve their coveted status. They both desperately want the world to stay the same and preserve their hegemony, but in reality they are sinking quickly along with the rest of the participants who are sinking faster than they are, thereby creating an illusion of their own success.

# Cooperation in a Declining Resource Base: Apples on an Island Metaphor

## Scenario 1

Can we cooperate in environments that are not conducive to cooperation, such as those of limited resources? To illustrate the question, I describe three scenarios. Scenario 1 follows:

- As a first scenario, suppose a shipwreck occurs on a deserted island without food. A sack of twelve apples remain from a shipwrecked group along with twelve people. They are desperately awaiting rescue and are starving.

- The "laws" of economics (supply and demand) do not apply in a declining resource base: panic usually sets in when the standard of living declines abruptly and significantly.

- How do they distribute the apples?

  » Divide them equally with one per person?

  » Do they hold a lottery to give all to one winner?

  » Do they vote who should make the decision?

  » Do they give the apples to women and children?

  » Do they give the apples to the person who owned the apples before the shipwreck?

  » Should the decision be unanimous, as infighting over the apples can expend energy and make matters worse for the starving individuals?

- Is it anti-capitalistic or "un-American" to make a unanimous group decision, such as in communism or socialism? Or should capitalism remain in place, and should we allow the person who owns the apples to decide what to do with them? We make critical, unanimous decisions everyday with a jury of twelve people without any explicit rules for them to convict a person of a crime. The rules are essentially set by the twelve jurors themselves.

- Virtually any argument for dividing these apples can be made and would seem rational. It doesn't matter what the group decides as long as the individuals on the island all agree with the process. Disagreements will ruin group cohesion and create resource shortages through conflict, which is a far greater expense to quell than the values of the apples themselves.

## Scenario 2

I propose a second scenario on that same island:

- In this scenario, the shipwreck has the same sack of twelve apples, but in addition the group now has several months' supply of rice and beans and an apple tree to plant.

- Who should tend to the apple tree? Does the distribution of the twelve apples change now that they are more a dessert than a subsistence-level food?

- When the apple tree bears fruit—perhaps in a few months—how should the apples be distributed?

  » According to Marx, the apple tree should be tended by the entire group and owned by no one. It is the group's tree.

  » Adam Smith may argue that of course the people who know the best farming techniques in this group should receive some benefit for their expertise as well as the person who owned the tree. For the pure capitalist, the person who owns the tree should hire the person with the expertise in the group to tend to the apple tree and be paid for his work. The problem is what or who determines that salary in this situation? Is it totally up to the person with the apple tree to decide who, if anyone else, gets the apples?

  » For the socialist, the group decides how to apportion the apples and this group decision can be made with the idea of apportioning a higher proportion of the apples to the individual who owns the tree and the individual who tended it. How should this decision come about, though? It is a crapshoot that cannot be determined scientifically or rationally. Never. It is a cultural value, not science. It is determined by our biosociophysical environment (which is irreducible)—something that science can never grasp.

- I argue that all three could, given the right biosociophysical environment, succeed. The key is not how the apportioning is done, but whether the entire group agrees. The key is whether we have conflict and accept the fact there are no laws of human behavior upon which to base our decision. All biosociophysical environments are unique and have unique conditions, making this question forever problematic. Economists and social scientists have been trying for the past couple hundred years to apply the scientific method to this question and it will never be answered. Human nature is too unpredictable to ever have a sufficient shadow to predict which system is the best.

- The success of the group will be more a function of the process of indoctrination of each member and how that system is determined rather than the distributive system itself. It is the cultural milieu that determines this system of distribution, not a predetermined factor like the environment or genetics.

- Resources play a huge factor in this process and the advantages bestowed on one system of distribution have to be accounted for with the ultimate foundation: systems succeed and fail based mainly upon the presence of apples, rice, beans, an apple tree, and the island one is stranded upon. Without any, some, or all of these resources, the method for distribution is irrelevant.

- The common thread for all successful social environments is *hope* for all members. When all members participate to make society successful, efficiencies are optimized because fewer resources are needed to control conflicting views. When members are estranged and do not feel like participants, regardless of whether they are efficient workers or not, the economics of a system will fail. The success of a system is strictly an *emotive variable* and not a calculation. A chain is only as strong as its weakest link; the Supercivilization is only as strong as its weakest member.

- Maximal disharmony occurs when more than one member harbors a different "view" or paradigm of what the biosociophysical environment means to them. A single member that is estranged from the group is easy to handle (or even multiple members with differing prions), but once a dissenting group establishes a common prion that runs counter to a preexisting prion, fundamental disharmony reaches critical dysfunction. Pretty soon the amount of resources produced is matched by the amount of resources needed merely to maintain harmony in the group. The civilization reaches a breaking point and can no longer function.

## Scenario 3

I propose a third scenario on this island:

- Suppose our twelve shipwrecked people are three families of four with only the twelve apples as food and nothing else.

- The families choose to live in three different huts in three different areas of the island. The families understand that family comes first and look out for family members especially.

- One family possesses all twelve of the apples, a second family has knowledge of the apples, and the third family has no idea apples exist.

- The family with knowledge of the apples asks the family with the apples to share them, without success. They then recruit the other family without the apples (and without knowledge that apples exist on the island) by telling them apples are harbored by the family with the apples. The two families join together to force the family with the apples to share. Conflict breaks out as eight hungry, starving individuals fight four others who are more energized and nutritionally advantaged individuals; this makes for maximal chaos.

- Far more resources are now being expended by all twelve members, as all twelve harbor different ideas of what is "correct." Two major paradigms or prions are squaring off, and it was only through the introduction of these paradigms that determined whether warfare or conflict breaks out. The four who knew the apples exist (but didn't have them) needed to convince those who had no knowledge of the apples to make conflict even possible. Ideas or culture plus knowledge (or Kantian interpretation of that environment) plus our institutions determine social cohesion and hence social success. The actual resources never changed, but the potential for conflict did, through our interpretation of that environment alone.

For conflict to be tenable, two sides with two separate ideas need to homogenize their views to fight a second prion. This conflict doesn't occur when a single paradigm or prion exists or if diverse prions refuse to homogenize. The only way to make this happen is crisis, as it polarizes and dichotomizes world views. This is the situation today (Phillip Zimbardo would call this situational attribution) with resource declines and the need to resolve problems that will lead to the potential demise of all humans. Today a dichotomy is now forming between haves and have-nots, as exemplified below:

- The First World has the apples.

- The Second World today knows and *cares* that the First World has the apples.

- The Third World today is oblivious to the apples, as they are trying to survive day to day. They are so overwhelmed with burdens they *don't understand or care*, as every day is a struggle. The Second World with its terrorists are recruiting and even manipulating those in the Third World to make their cause more successful.

## The Prion of Anthropocentricity: Our Hurdle

To optimize our chances, we must unify, coordinate, and cooperate to avoid self-annihilation—we must embrace the global realization that we control our future. Our biggest hurdle is now promoting the right prion that will maximize our chances for survival. This is difficult. A larger, more difficult prion now exists and must be eliminated:

- The Prion of Anthropocentricity has existed for centuries, and we must overcome this. We are currently infected with this prion, and now we must instill a new prion to counter it. Those who follow this prion believe humans have a manifest destiny to encroach on the Universe because the Universe was created by humans and for humans. Individuals have a higher cause than the material environment surrounding us, as death brings salvation. Our Universe becomes expendable, as its place is not the centerpiece of our existence.

- The major problem with this prion is that it is based on thinking that the will of God is written into nonmodifiable sacred documents. These documents can then be taken literally or converted into figurative translations. Either way, the dynamism of the Supercivilization is so great that sacred documents make coping with this hyperdynamism nearly impossible. No one can rationally argue against an irrationally based prion, and as a result, changing someone's mind is nearly impossible. Newer generations of people instilled with a better prion must now be instituted for our survival.

## The Development of the Prion of Universe Centricity

The key to our survival will to be to instill the Prion of Universe Centricity into all humans, thereby replacing the Prion of Anthropocentricity.

- This prion is a realization that the well-being of the here and now (the material world) supersedes all values. This Universe is our only reason for existence and supersedes a higher calling or purpose which cannot be empirically verified. The Universe created us; we didn't create the Universe.

- It is unlikely that this prion can be established in an individual already infected with the Prion of Anthropocentricity, as they are irrationally based polar opposites. As a result, instilling this value in young and disenfranchised individuals is crucial for our survival.

- If individuals adhere to this prion, it is less likely that those individuals will be manipulated by those interests who want to preserve the status quo at the expense of the Supercivilization. Those minority interests who manipulate the meaning of success (they call it a higher calling or value) will be likely to perform masterfully while using the Prion of Anthropocentricity as a tool. For those who adopt the Prion of Universe Centricity and treat our existence as definitive and a beginning and end unto itself, the aforementioned manipulation is less likely to be successful.

- The Supercivilization as a subcategory of our Universe must be our primary focus. When others are distracted from this goal, we will lose focus, and suicide will seem the best of many options.

## Prion of Anthropocentricity

The Universe is created specifically for the human being. This prion focuses on salvation and the existence of a higher calling for each individual. It is divorced from reality. It is the most dangerous prion, and it can infect all of us.

## Prion of Universe Centricity

The human being is created as an incidental part of the Universe. This prion focuses on the here and now. It is based on empirical reality, nothing more.

# The Vaccine Paradox Model: Our Achilles Heel

Is there ever a time when an act that benefits the common good but puts the individual at more personal risk is the best decision for that individual? That depends. Vaccinations could be used to exemplify the paradox.

- When vaccines were first introduced two hundred years ago, our ability to fight disease required 100 percent group cooperation. Huge success was achieved, as vaccinations have virtually eliminated several diseases (Figure 11.1).

- Today many vaccines are viewed by some as being dangerous for the individual simply because they are thinking in terms of individual risk. They see the vaccine's side effects as being greater than the chance of acquiring the disease.

- If one is thinking only in terms of group risk, the vaccination is clearly beneficial.

- The vaccine is so effective (and group cooperation is so effective) that the vaccine itself becomes the problem in the minds of many because there is no recent history of how devastating the diseases that vaccines protected

| Disease | Reporting Period | Annual Morbidity Prior to Vaccine | 2001 Morbidity | 2002 Morbidity[a] | Decrease, %[b] |
|---|---|---|---|---|---|
| Smallpox | 1900–1904 | 48,164 | 0 | 0 | 100 |
| Diptheria | 1920–1922 | 175,885 | 2 | 1 | 100 |
| Pertussis | 1922–1925 | 147,271 | 7,580 | 8,296 | 94.6 |
| Tetanus | 1922–1926 | 1,314 | 27 | 23 | 98.1 |
| Poliomyelitis (paralytic) | 1951–1954 | 16,316 | 0 | 0 | 100 |
| Measles | 1958–1962 | 503,282 | 116 | 37 | 99.9 |
| Mumps | 1968 | 152,209 | 266 | 238 | 99.8 |
| Rubella | 1966–1968 | 47,745 | 23 | 14 | 99.9 |
| Congenital Rubella Syndrome | 1969 | 823 | 3 | 3 | 99.6 |
| Haemophilus influenzae type b | Before 1985 | 20,000 | 27 | 27 | 99.6 |

[a] Provisional data.
[b] Average of figures for 2001 and 2002 compared with peak incidence.

FIGURE 11.1   Reduction in Morbidity Due to Vaccine-Preventable Diseases in the United States, 1900–2002

The Supercivilization: Essential Concepts

against can be. Similarly, as a general rule, group success reduces so much pathology that the side effects of group success become the problem.

- We have done such an effective job at eliminating real pathology through group cooperation that the current pathology that we see around us becomes an illusion of catastrophe. This illusory pathology (pseudopathology) is making our abilities to fight real pathology troublesome.

- It was the unanimous group cooperation in the first place that led to the decline of disease, thus making the individual's risk *only seem greater from taking the vaccine.*

- This is similar to the conservative who complains that "government gets in my way" when in fact without universal cooperation (and the government itself) the individual wouldn't have the ability to achieve optimally at the individual level.

- In spite of one's suspicions, the individual is not constrained by group cooperation; he is empowered by it. This is the vaccine paradox of self-sacrifice.

Chapter 12

# Our Last Hope:
# Global Action

"None of the upheavals will happen spontaneously. ... Governments will not act on our behalf until we force them to do so. The political classes from which most governing parties are drawn have no interest in this revolution. ... Our global revolution requires no tumbrils, no guillotines, no unmarked graves; no revanchist running dogs need be put against the wall. We have within our hands already the means to a peaceful, demo-cratic transformation."

—*George Monbiot, author of* Manifesto for a New World Order

# Climate Change: No Progress

We can do all the theorizing we want, but unless real change occurs with real solutions, our progress is noncontributory. Climate change is our Mt. Toba.

- Our progress on climate change (no firm targets for reducing carbon emissions) has been minimal:

  » 2009 Copenhagen summit was a major disappointment. No definitive targets were set.

  » 2010 Cancun summit was unproductive. No definitive targets were set.

  » 2011 Durban summit was unproductive. No definitive targets were set.

  » 2012 Rio summit was unproductive. No definitive targets were set.

  » 2012 Doha summit was unproductive. No definitive targets were set.

- World leaders are not necessarily causing the failure; the parameters that the leaders must work in are too confining. The institutions are not conducive to good leadership on universal issues that require mandatory cooperation. Nation-state sovereignty still trumps humanitarian concerns.

- Meaningful consensus can never be achieved through our current nation-state paradigm.

- Progress on our most critical problem—climate change—is impossible without an overarching system that promotes the establishment, procurement, and enforcement of major solutions that affect us all. Climate change is humanity's first major problem that has required universal cooperation from all 7 billion people.

# Still a Significant Mountain to Climb

Of course, not everyone will agree that global governance and unity is the answer to our most serious problems:

- The extremist Tea Party is seeking problematic solutions appropriate for a time of less interconnectedness. They are seeking solutions for a 20th century United States not a 21st century Supercivilization. They are seeking to do the following:

  » Promote less equality, less government, and a balanced budget amendment.

  » Eliminate the role of the federal reserve. The $14.3 billion debt ceiling was recently raised after tremendous struggle and protest by a Tea

Party faction in Congress. This rattled global markets, as uncertainty replaced a routine mechanism.

» Castrate the institution of last resort—the federal government—for protecting against an economic meltdown. To stave off economic collapse (Keynesian economics) in a capitalist system, the protector of last resort must be the government.

» Castrate an institution that will referee competition to make the playing field more level. With less government in an interconnected world, vested interests will be free to manipulate the poor and create massive disparities in wealth.

- A comprehensive change involving economic, sociological, and political institutions must take place for the Supercivilization to survive. Anything short of this comprehensive change will leave grave defects that will swallow our Supercivilization whole.

- A change in these institutions must allow us to create a safe and effective prion controlled by us, not malevolent interests. With this interconnectedness, the most basic unit of success is not the individual but the Supercivilization.

» Descartes stated, "I think therefore I am." We must say, "We think therefore we are."

» The scientific community agrees with Descartes. The journal *Science* stated in its December 11, 2009 issue, "The betterment of humankind depends on a deliberate move from being an international community of scientists to being a truly global community."

## Fundamental Steps Needed to Protect the Supercivilization from Self-Annihilation

Six steps are necessary for our survival as a species. None have been accomplished yet:

1. **Realization**

2. **Correct prioritization of the pathology**

3. **Identification of the correct etiology of the pathology**

4. **Unification**

5. **Political pressure**

6. **Real global action**

## Step 1. Realization

We must realize that if we do nothing, we are in serious danger of a catastrophic die-off.

- We must adopt the Prion of Universe Centricity; if not we are likely to fail. Too much social pathology, mainly involving battles between individuals infected with opposing and irrationally based prions, could lead to a Class VIII Event.

- Complete unification, enfranchisement, and cooperation are the foundation of any solutions to our pathology. There will always be the issue of rogue individuals to address, but as a unified front, that battle will be minimal.

- Climate change is the supreme and defining challenge of our day, but even more pathology will ensue if we do not adopt the Prion of Universe Centricity immediately.

## Step 2. Correct Prioritization of the Pathology

We must focus on the pathology that is truly pathological and of the most consequence to us as a species.

- While there are countless problems, we must focus on those that need immediate resolution.

- Please, no more tetanus shots! We need a surgeon to operate on an ailing Supercivilization.

- Social problems are languishing because of vested interests who prefer the personal benefits of the status quo to the universal benefits for all humankind.

- Four problems demand immediate attention and resolution:

  » Human population control

  » Resource utilization and emission control

  » Setting minimum standards for world and individual health, with constitutionally protected health care for everyone

  » Reducing disparities in per capita wealth

## Step 3. Identification of the Correct Etiology of the Pathology

Not just the pathology, but the cause of the pathology must be clearly identified. This is again a challenge.

- The underlying foundation for much of our pathology is the competitive imbalance in the world and the lack of a level playing field.

- Coordinated, balanced efforts are mandatory. An ad hoc approach by independently studying each problem is wasteful and even self-defeating. Vested interests prefer this approach because it is an easier argument to defend against.

- With a current political system that allows the agenda to be dictated by vested interests, the correct etiology will never be discussed or publicly contemplated. The need for a constitutionally protected limit to corporate participation in elections will help identify both the most dangerous pathology and its cause.

- The use of fossil fuels is our most pressing problem, yet serious attempts to quickly resolve its consequential problem—$CO_2$ waste emissions—are lacking. This is the classic case of the energy industrial complex preserving its standing by looking for other, more mysterious causes of climate change.

## Step 4. Unification

With a declining resource base, increased interconnectedness, and increased disparities in wealth, unification is critical.

- Unifying with one set of rules with one culture is a foregone conclusion. It has occurred, but we still don't recognize this as such.

- In the past, personal liberty has been essential, but personal freedoms now impinge on others in a highly interconnected world.

- Unless we suddenly make major technological changes, we are stuck with high-density living.

- Promotion of trust will be a key factor in unification; without trust we cannot unify. Trust is slowly being lost as our interconnectedness rises. For example, in 1960, 58 percent of Americans felt other people could be trusted; by 1993, that figure dropped to 37 percent.

- Robert Axelrod has identified the best way to promote trust (Figure 12.1). In a high ICQ/ITQ world, intrinsic trust (trust formulated through repeated interactions by the same individuals) is dissipating; extrinsic trust (trust enforced through institutions such as government through laws) is replacing this. The only way to universally promote extrinsic trust is through a global government that has full universal authority to maintain this trust.

| A COMPARISON OF THE THREE BIOSOCIOPHYSICAL ERAS | | | |
|---|---|---|---|
| | **First Era of Humanity** | **Second Era of Humanity** | **Third Era of Humanity** |
| All Social Interactions with Others | Personal | Mostly personal and some impersonal interactions | Mostly impersonal |
| Extent of Network Needed for Exchange of Goods/ Services | Simple effective | Simple and complex | Extensive |
| Nature of Social Interactions Involved in Resource Procurement and Problem Solving | Hopelessly repetitive with same individuals | Mixture of repetitive exchanges with same individuals and anonymous individuals | Primarily anonymous and distant interactions |
| Major Type of Promotion/ Enforcement for Intrinsic Trust* | Repetitive reciprocal exchanges for mutual benefit | Repetitive reciprocal exchanges and formal laws by state | Formal laws by state |
| Level of Intrinsic Trust within our Social Relationships | Significant | Less significant | Minimally significant |
| Necessary Institutional Support to Maintain/Supplement Intrinsic Trust | None | Tribe to nation-state | Global government |

* Robert Axelrod has argued that trust is created through "frequent and durable interactions among specific individuals." I define this as intrinsic trust. Intrinsic trust is created with others and is based solely on those repeated interactions that are mutually beneficial. Extrinsic trust (in what Axelrod calls an 'external authority')is generated by a central authority that enforces and promotes the intrinsic trust. Axelrod argues that most of the time the mere threat of extrinsic action is enough to promote intrinsic trust. We gain trust in our social relations when there is a history of successful and predictable interactions that are mutually beneficial regardless of their origin (extrinsic or intrinsic). Today, our world lacks appropriate extrinsic authority to enforce and promote declining intrinsic trust because of our massively increased interconnectedness.

FIGURE 12.1 Promotion/Enforcement of Trust: Foundation for Effective Resource Procurement and Problem Solving

## Step 5. Political Pressure

The only mechanism to use for creating real global action is political pressure.

- Current leadership and political institutions are unacceptably corrupt in large areas of the world. In some areas, like Somalia and Afghanistan, leadership is virtually nonexistent.

- As long as half the world remains disenfranchised, we will never hold our leaders accountable, making political pressure unrealistic.

- Transparency International's Corruption Perception Index shows corruption is still rampant throughout the world:

  » Seven out of ten countries of the world were very corrupt (scored less than 5 out of 10).

  » The world's two most populous countries, India and China, accounting for a third of the world's population, scored an unacceptable 3.3 and 3.5 respectively.

- A four branch government including an independent health care branch and a constitution with a full Bill of Rights must take place to allow for accountability to all humans regardless of geographical origin.

## Step 6. Real Global Action

Until we see real global action, our world could end in a Class VIII Event. Here is what we can do:

- Install a global government (United States of Mother Earth or the like) through Project Alliance over the next 10 years.

- Much of the $2.1 trillion spent on military budgets annually in the United States can be freed to resolve waste emissions and resource utilization problems, global health problems, population growth problems, and terrorism.

- Removing individuals from extreme poverty (three billion people living on less than $2.50 per day) will help resolve many of the world's problems without having to sacrifice living standards. This can be done through a global tax.

- By exporting medicine, food, and supplies instead of guns and ammunition to the Third World, the First World will decrease social pathology to the point of irrelevance for the entire world. This could be funded through a global tax and a constitutionally-protected fourth branch of government.

- We need to dedicate a huge percentage of our GWP (Gross World Product) to creating massive changes in our global energy infrastructure to encourage near total elimination (at least an 85 percent reduction from 1990 levels) of carbon emissions by 2040. This solution could include sequestration, if the technology is affordable and is not environmentally damaging.

- We can create an immediate and graduated carbon tax (an immediate 50 to 100 percent increase in cost to the consumer) should be implemented to fund this new technology. New forms of carbon-free technology, such as new forms of nuclear power and a new Smart Grid to promote green technology, should be implemented to reduce inefficiencies.

- We can immediately freeze the growth of all fossil fuel use until the effectiveness of carbon sequestration can be demonstrated successfully. If it cannot in perhaps 5 years, then a mandatory global decline of fossil fuel use (starting with the greatest $CO_2$ emitters like coal) should begin.

"I am not an advocate for frequent changes in laws and constitutions. But laws and institutions must go hand in hand with the progress of the human mind. As that becomes more developed, more enlightened, as new discoveries are made, new truths discovered and manners and opinions change, with the change of circumstances, institutions must advance also to keep pace with the times. We might as well require a man to wear still the coat which fitted him when a boy as civilized society to remain ever under the regimen of their barbarous ancestors."

*—From a letter written by Thomas Jefferson on July 12, 1816, to Samuel Kercheval and inscribed in the Jefferson Memorial*

E PLURIBUS UNUM

*... included in the Seal of the United States of America.*

# APPENDIX

| Time | Population Estimate | Separation of Most Distant Inhabitants (kilometers) | Communication | | ICQ |
|---|---|---|---|---|---|
| | | | Method | Total Time (seconds) | |
| 4,000,000 years ago[2] | <1,000,000[5] | 4,000 | Walking | 2,880,000 | 2.33 x 10⁻⁹ |
| 1,000,000 years ago[3] | <1,000,000[5] | 15,000 | Walking | 10,800,000 | 26.21 x 10⁻¹⁰ |
| 100,000 years ago[4] | <1,000,000[5] | 6,000 | Walking | 4,320,000 | 1.51 x 10⁻⁹ |
| 12,000 years ago | 1,000,000 | 30,000[6] | Walking | 21,600,000 | 3.11 x 10⁻¹⁰ |
| At birth of Christ | 100,000,000 | 30,000[6] | Horse | 5,400,000 | 1.24 x 10⁻⁷ |
| 1000 AD | 310,000,000 | 30,000[6] | Horse | 5,400,000 | 3.85 x 10⁻⁷ |
| 1900 AD | 1,600,000,000 | 20,000 | Telegraph | 60 | 1.179 |
| 1950 AD | 2,500,000,000 | 20,000 | Telegraph, radio | 3 | 5.59 |
| 2000 AD | 6,000,000,000 | 20,000 | Internet | 3 | 13.4 |

1  149 million km³ land surface area on Earth.
2  *Ardipithecus ramidus* was present around 4 million years ago when humans first walked upright.
3  *Homo erectus* existed from 1.8 million years ago to 300,000 years ago and migrated out of Africa to southern Eurasia.

FIGURE APP.1  Detailed Analysis of the Relative Interconnectedness of Past and Present Humanity (people/km³-seconds) and Survivability from Resource Depletion [people-years)/(km³-seconds)][1]

| Transportation | | | ITQ | Years to Survival at Per Capita Resource Use | Resource Survivability Index |
| --- | --- | --- | --- | --- | --- |
| Velocity (km/hr) | Method | Total Time (seconds) | | | |
| 5 | Walking | 2,880,000 | $2.33 \times 10^{-9}$ | Near infinite | >1,000,000 |
| 5 | Walking | 10,000,000 | $6.21 \times 10^{-10}$ | Near infinite | >1,000,000 |
| 5 | Walking | 4,320,000 | $1.55 \times 10^{-9}$ | Near infinite | >1,000,000 |
| 5 | Walking | 21,600,000 | $3.11 \times 10^{-10}$ | Near infinite | >1,000,000 |
| 20 | Horse | 5,400,000 | $1.24 \times 10^{-7}$ | Near infinite | >1,000,000 |
| 20 | Horse | 5,400,000 | $3.85 \times 10^{-7}$ | Near infinite | >1,000,000 |
| 40 | Ship & horse | 1,800,000 | $5.97 \times 10^{-5}$ | 120 | 21.5 |
| 1,000 | Jet plane at mach 1–2 with helicopter transfer | 72,000 | $2.33 \times 10^{-4}$ | 70 | 391 |
| 10,000 | Space shuttle and jet plane/ helicopter transfer | 7,200 | $5.59 \times 10^{-3}$ | 20 | 268 |

4  *Homo sapiens sapiens* (modern humans) existed from 200,000 years ago to present—migrated only slightly out of Africa to South Central Asia.

5  Even though most demographers are not sure of the population size before 10,000 BC, most would concur there were probably at most 1,000,000 hominins.

6  Even though the Earth is 40,000 km in circumference, it would have been roughly 30,000 km by foot given travel only by land and not by sea at that time.

FIGURE A.1 (cont'd)

# Figure Credits and Sources of Data for Figures

FIGURE 1.1     Designed by Sara Waters. Source: Author's estimates.

FIGURE 1.2     Designed by Sara Waters.

FIGURE 1.3     Designed by Sara Waters. Source: Author's estimates.

FIGURE 1.4     Designed by Jimmie Young. Source: Author's estimates.

FIGURE 2.1     Designed by Jimmie Young and Sara Waters. Source: Author's estimates.

FIGURE 2.2 A     Designed by Sara Waters. Source: Author's estimates.

FIGURE 2.2 B and C     Designed by Sara Waters.
Source: US Census Bureau. 2013. "World Population: Historical Estimates of World Population." Accessed July 12. http://www.census.gov/population/international/data/worldpop/table_history.php.

FIGURE 2.2 D     Designed by Sara Waters. Sources: US Census Bureau. 2013. "World Population: Historical Estimates of World Population." Accessed July 12. http://www.census.gov/population/international/data/worldpop/table_history.php.

Population Reference Bureau. 2013. "World Population Growth, 1950-2050." Accessed July 12. http://www.prb.org/Educators/TeacherGuides/HumanPopulation/PopulationGrowth.aspx.

FIGURE 2.2 E     Designed by Sara Waters. Source: Author's estimates.

FIGURES 3.1 and 3.2     Designed by Sara Waters.
Sources: Centers for Disease Control and Prevention. 1999. "Achievements in Public Health, 1900-99: Healthier Mothers and Babies." Morbidity and Mortality Weekly Report. Oct. 1; 48(38):849-58. http://www.cdc.gov/mmwr/preview/mmwrhtml/mm4838a2.htm.

Centers for Disease Control and Prevention. 2011. "Leading Causes of Death 1900-98," Tables 1-8,15,288,L. Accessed May 2. http://www.cdc.gov/nchs/data/dvs/lead1900_98.pdf.

US Department of Health and Human Services. 2006. *National Vital Statistics Reports.* June 28; 54(19). Washington DC: US Government Printing Office. Accessed Sep 20, 2011. http://www.infoplease.com/ipa/A0005140.html.

Haines, M. 2010. "Fertility and Mortality in the United States." Economic History Association. Posted Feb. 4. http://eh.net/encyclopedia/article/haines.demography.

Wegman, M.E. 2001. "Infant Mortality in the 20th Century, Dramatic but Uneven Progress." *Journal of Nutrition*131(2):4015-85.

Branum, A.M. 2013. "Infant Mortality in the US: An Introductory Exploration." National Center for Health Statistics, Infant and Child Health Studies Branch. Accessed July 12. http://www.iom.edu/~/media/Files/Activity%20Files/PublicHealth/ImmunizationSafety/Branum.ashx.

MacDorman, M.F., D.L. Hoyert, and T.J. Matthews. 2008. "Recent Declines in Infant Mortality in the United States, 2005-2011." National Center for Health Statistics Data Brief No. 120. http://www.cdc.gov/nchs/data/databriefs/db120.pdf.

| FIGURES 3.3 and 3.4 | Designed by Sara Waters.<br>Source: Centers for Disease Control and Prevention. 2011. "Leading Causes of Death 1900-98," Tables 1–8,15,288,L. Accessed May 2. http://www.cdc.gov/nchs/data/dvs/lead1900_98.pdf. |
|---|---|
| FIGURE 3.5 | Designed by Sara Waters. Sources: Centers for Disease Control and Prevention. 2013. "Years of Potential Life Lost Before Age 75 for Selected Causes of Death, by Sex, Race, and Hispanic Origin: United States, Selected Years 1986-2006," Table 29. Accessed July 14. ftp://ftp.cdc.gov/pub/health_statistics/nchs/Publications/.../Table029.xls.<br><br>Centers for Disease Control and Prevention. 2013. "Health, United States, 2012," Table 21. Last modified May 30. http://www.cdc.gov/nchs/data/hus/2012/021.pdf.<br><br>Pamuk, E., D. Makuc, K. Heck, et al. 1998. "Health, United States, 1998: With Socioeconomic Status and Health Chartbook." *US Department of Health and Human Services*. Washington DC: US Government Printing Office. |
| FIGURE 3.6 | Redesigned by Sara Waters. Source: World Health Organization. 2007. "Spending on Health: A Global Overview." Posted Feb. http://www.who.int/mediacentre/factsheets/fs319.pdf. |
| FIGURE 3.7 | Redesigned by Sara Waters. Source: Executive Office of the President, Council of Economic Advisers, 2009; Organisation for Economic Co operation and Development, 2008. |
| FIGURE 4.1 | Designed by Sara Waters. Source: Maddison, A. 2009. "Historical Statistics for the World Economy: 1–2003 AD." Accessed March 9. www.ggdc.net/maddison/historical_statistics/horizontal-file_03-2007.xls. |
| FIGURE 4.2 and 4.3 | Designed by Sara Waters.<br>Source: Central Intelligence Agency. 2012. "The World Factbook: Country Comparison—GDP per Capita (PPP)." Accessed Nov. 29. https://www.cia.gov/library/publications/the-world-factbook/rankorder/2004rank.html. |
| FIGURE 4.4 | Designed by Sara Waters. Sources: Central Intelligence Agency. 2012. "The World Factbook: Country Comparison—GDP per Capita (PPP)." Accessed Nov. 29. https://www.cia.gov/library/publications/the-world-factbook/rankorder/2004rank.html.<br><br>Central Intelligence Agency. 2012. "The World Factbook: Country Comparison—Infant Mortality Rate." Accessed Nov. 29. https://www.cia.gov/library/publications/the-world-factbook/rankorder/2091rank.html.<br><br>Central Intelligence Agency. 2012. "The World Factbook: Country Comparison—Life Expectancy at Birth." Accessed Nov. 29. https://www.cia.gov/library/publications/the-world-factbook/fields/2102.html. |
| FIGURE 4.5 | Designed by Sara Waters. Source: Anon. 2006. "Europe #1 in Per Capita Cell Phone Usage." Posted Feb. 28. http://www.etforecasts. com/pr/pr206.htm. |
| FIGURE 4.6 | Redesigned by Sara Waters. Sources: Anon. 2012. "File: TFR vs PPP 2009.svg." Accessed Mar 29. http://commons.wikimedia.org /wiki/File:TFR _vsPPP_2009.svg.<br><br>Central Intelligence Agency. 2012. "The World Factbook: Country Comparison—GDP per Capita (PPP)." Accessed Nov. 29. https://www.cia.gov/library/publications/the-world-factbook/rankorder/2004rank.html.<br><br>Central Intelligence Agency. 2012. "The World Factbook: Country Comparison—Total Fertility Rate." Accessed Nov. 29. https://www.cia.gov/library/publications/the-world-factbook/rankorder/2127rank.html. |
| FIGURE 5.1 | Designed by Sara Waters. Source: Author's estimates. |
| FIGURE 5.2 | Designed by Sara Waters. Source: Author's estimates. |
| FIGURE 5.3 | Designed by Sara Waters. Source: Author's estimates. |

FIGURE 6.1 A    Redesigned by Sara Waters. Sources: Erwin, D. H. 2006. *Extinction: How Life on Earth Nearly Ended 250 Million Years Ago*. Princeton, NJ: Princeton University Press. 29.

Sepkoski, J. J. 1984. "A Kinetic Model of Phanerozoic Taxonomic Diversity; III Post-Paleozoic Families and Mass Extinctions." Paleobiology. 10:229–245.

FIGURE 6.1 B    Redesigned by Sara Waters. Sources: Erwin, D. H. 2006. *Extinction: How Life on Earth Nearly Ended 250 Million Years Ago*. Princeton, NJ: Princeton University Press. 31.

Raup, D. 1991. *Extinction: Bad Genes or Bad Luck?* New York: W. W. Norton. 81.

FIGURE 6.1 C    Redesigned by Sara Waters. Sources: Erwin, D. H. 2006. *Extinction: How Life on Earth Nearly Ended 250 Million Years Ago*. Princeton, NJ: Princeton University Press. 32.

Raup, D. M., and J. J. Sepkoski. 1986. "Periodic Extinction of Family and Genera." Science. 231(4740):833–6.

FIGURE 6.2    Designed by Sara Waters. Source: Source: Bennett, J., and S. Shostak. 2007. *Life in the Universe*. 2nd Edition. San Francisco: Pearson Addison Wesley. 364.

FIGURE 6.3    Redesigned by Sara Waters. Source: Source: Nelson, S. 2012. "Meteorites, Impacts, and Mass Extinction." Last modified July 17. http://www.tulane.edu/~sanelson/Natural_Disasters/impacts.htm.

FIGURE 7.1    Designed by Sara Waters. Source: Author's estimates.

FIGURE 7.2 A    Designed by Sara Waters. Source: Author's estimates.

FIGURES 7.2 B    Designed by Sara Waters.
and 7.2 C    Sources: US Department of Health and Human Services. 2006. National Vital Statistics Reports. June 28; 54(19). Washington DC: US Government Printing Office. Accessed Sep 20, 2011. http://www.infoplease.com/ipa/A0005140.html.

Simanis, J. G., and J. R. Coleman. 1980. "Health Care Expenditures in Nine Industrialized Counties, 1960–76." Social Security Bulletin. January; 43(1).

Martin, A. B., L. S. Whittle, and K. R. Levit. 2001. "Trends in State Health Care Expenditures and Funding: 1980-1998." Health Care Financing Review. 22(4):111-140. http://www.cms.gov/Research-Statistics-Data-and-Systems/Research/HealthCareFinancingReview/do.

World Health Organization. 2008. "Total Health Expenditures as % of GDP, 2002–2005." Last modified Oct. 4. http://www.photius.com/rankings/total_health_expenditure_as_pecent_of_gdp_2000_to_2005.html.

FIGURE 7.3    Source: Dustin © 2012 Steve Kelley & Jeff Parker. King Features Syndicate.

FIGURE 7.4    Designed by Jimmie Young. Source: Lopez, A. D., C. D. Mathers, M. Ezzati, D. T. Jamison, and C. J. L. Murray, eds. 2006. "Chapter 1: Measuring the Global Burden of Disease and Risk Factors, 1990-2001."

In Lopez, et al., eds, 2006, 1–13. 8.

FIGURE 8.1    Designed by Sara Waters. Source: Author's estimates.

FIGURE 8.2    Redesigned by Sara Waters.
A to C    Sources: Center for Climate and Energy Solutions. 2012. "Atmospheric Carbon Dioxide and Global Surface Temperature Trends." Accessed April 8. http://www.c2es.org/facts-figures/trends/co2-temp.

_____. 2012. "Historical Global CO2 Emissions." Accessed April 8. http://www.c2es.org/facts- figures/international-emissions/historical.

_____. 2012. "International Annual GHG Emissions." Accessed April 8. http://www.c2es.org/ facts-figures/international-emissions/annual-ghg.

FIGURE 8.3    Redesigned by Sara Waters. Source: Jansen, E., and J. Overpeck. 2007. "Paleoclimate." In Solomon, S. D., et al. 2007. (Contribution of Working Group I to the Fourth Assessment Report of the Intergovernmental Panel on Climate Change, 2007; 467).

| FIGURE 8.4 | Redesigned by Sara Waters. Sources: National Oceanic and Atmospheric Administration. 2013. "Global Ocean Heat and Salt Content." Last modified May 29. http://www.nodc.noaa.gov/OC5/3M_HEAT_CONTENT/. |
|---|---|
| | Levitus, S., J. L. Antonov, T. P. Boyer, et al. 2012. "World Ocean Heat Content and Thermosteric Sea Level Change (0–2000 m), 1955–2010." *Geophysical Research Letters*. 39(L10603):1–26. |
| FIGURE 8.5 | Redesigned by Sara Waters. Source: US Environmental Protection Agency. 2013. "Climate Change—Science Figure 1: Changes in Carbon Dioxide and Temperature." Last modified June 21. http://www.epa.gov/climatechange/science/pastcc_fig1.html. |
| FIGURE 8.6 | Redesigned by Sara Waters. Source: Bures, P. 2006. *America: The Oil Hostage*. College Station, TX: Virtualbookworm.com Publishing. 28. |
| FIGURE 8.7 | Redesigned by Sara Waters. Source: Bures, P. 2006. *America: The Oil Hostage*. College Station, TX: Virtualbookworm.com Publishing. 30. |
| FIGURE 8.8 | Redesigned by Sara Waters. Source: Bures, P. 2006. *America: The Oil Hostage*. College Station, TX: Virtualbookworm.com Publishing. 106. |
| FIGURE 9.1 | Designed by Jimmie Young. |
| FIGURE 10.1 | Designed by Sara Waters. Source: Author's estimates. |
| FIGURE 10.2 | Designed by Sara Waters. Source: Author's estimates. |
| FIGURE 10.3 | Designed by Sara Waters.  Source: Author's estimates. |
| FIGURE 11.1 | Redesigned by Jimmie Young. Source: Kasper, D. L., A. S. Fauci, D. L. Long, E. Braunwald, S. L. Hauser, and J. L. Jameson, eds. 2005. *Harrison's Principles of Internal Medicine*. 16th Edition. New York: McGraw-Hill. 713. |
| FIGURE 12.1 | Designed by Sara Waters. |
| FIGURE APP.1 | Designed by Sara Waters. Source: Author's estimates. |

# Index to General Concepts, Sidebar Terms, and Quotes

disease
    aging and  115
    burden versus lethality  115
    continuous nature  112
    curing  109
    defining  112
    efficacy  111
    nature of  107
    resource expenditure  111
    as survival indicators  116–123
    today's  108
    Western  110
disparity in wealth  2
drug use  62
Durkheim, Èmile  xvii

# E

egalitarian existence  24
Emanuel, Ezekiel  106
E=MC$^2$  59
energy problems  145, 146
evapotranspiration  34
event classes
    definition  92
    independent  91
    interdependent  93
events, problems and  97
"Everyone is entitled ..."  96
"Extraordinary times ..."  xviii

# F

failed civilizations  77
first biosociophysical era
    described  2, 20
    human beings  23
    major concerns  22
First Era of Humanity, nature dependent  16
fossil fuels  143, 148
Francis, Blake  132

# G

gamma-ray bursts  98
gas  150
Genesis  16
global action  208
global governance  209
global government  6, 83
global realization  188
"God said ... be fruitful ..."  16
golden hour  75
growth, exponential  143

# H

health care
    difficulties  122
    individual rights versus societal rights  124
    more is better?  128
    refusing  127
herd effect  142, 171
Hitler  59, 190
HIV  119, 125
Hominin History  14–15
hominins  18
human and nature dependent  26, 48
human dependent  74
human-induced problems
    primarily  132
    purely  154
Humans for a Healthier World  232
human versus nature  24

# I

ICQ  21
    *See also* interconnectedness
ideas  50
"If it walks like a duck ..."  13
"If mankind could so quickly destroy ..."  188
"If you hear hoofbeats, ..."  85
illusion of need  111, 131
inanimate  18
individual success  75
industrial revolution  44
information sharing  24
"In practice, we don't automatically have
    dominion; ..."  16
interconnectedness
    biosociophysical eras and  20, 22
    catastrophe and  46, 156, 160
    defined  3
    economy and  58
    idea sharing and  52, 171
    illusion of need and  111
    malevolence and  64, 91
    measures of  21
    population growth and  42, 43
    pre-10,000 BC  17, 24
    relationship to Supercivilization  2, 155
    science and  54
    terrorists and  193
    viruses and  163
irrationality
    logic and  141
    medicine and  65
    powerful interests and  30
    and rationality paradox  27
    religion and  30
"It ain't what you don't know ..."  86

society versus societal subculture 125
society versus the sociopathic individual 125
sociological being 30
sociologically modern human 49
socioplacebo-like effect 184, 185
sports as a metaphor
    about 195
    Major League Baseball 198
    National Basketball Association 197
    National Football League 196
success, individual and societal 75
Supercivilization
    about 2
    birth of 155
    fundamental steps to save 210–215
supernova explosions 97, 98
supervolcano explosions
    about 97, 104
    frequency and odds 105
Survivability Index 21, 22
survival, best model for 157
Swiss-Cheese model 87, 171
synergistic catastrophe 170

## T

Tainter, Joseph 26
tale of two civilizations 41
Tatersall, Ian 16
terrorism 77
"The spread of information ..." 74
"The success of the United States ..." 187
third biosociophysical era
    described 2, 20
    major concerns 22
third era of humanity 74
time 189
tipping points 172
tobacco addiction 61, 126
transistor problem-solving model 90
treatment disparities 107
tuberculosis 118
Twain, Mark 86
Typhoid Mary 125

## U

universal cooperation 28
unpredictability 168

## V

vaccine paradox model 206
virus (as social metaphor) 159, 162, 163
volatility of markets 76
Volcanic Explosive Index 32

## W

Ward, Peter 188

water, lack of 133
wealth disparities 2
worms (as social metaphor) 158–159, 161

## Z

Zakaria, Fareed 154

# About the
# Mission Statement

John Moser theorizes that humanity is faced with the distinct possibility of self-annihilation, which has never before existed. With a declining resource base, increasing interconnectedness, and tremendous disparities in wealth, humanity today is experiencing a potentially noxious combination of factors that will make avoiding self-annihilation extremely difficult.

Moser argues that the only way to deal with this situation is to immediately create a strong global government and enfranchise all seven billion humans. He argues that giving all people (not just those with the power to capitalize on an immediate self-interest) the power to determine the future of humanity will be the key to survival. Putting human and environmental health first will be critical.

He is proposing the Mission Statement for Humanity (see pp. 4–5). This is a ten-point plan that outlines an immediate need to acknowledge the existence of the one civilization that we all are part of today, called the Supercivilization. Once we acknowledge this, we can then make significant changes in our problem solving to create real solutions and not merely pseudosolutions. For the first time, natural problems have been drowned out by the social problems of what Moser calls the sociologically modern human. The social problems become far more difficult to resolve in a world with so much interconnectedness, so many limited resources, and such disparities in wealth that he fears until we align our institutions to match the needs of sociologically modern humans, we could be in for a major human-induced catastrophe. Moser does not want to see that happen. Do you? If you feel the same way, sign the Mission Statement for Humanity now at *www.msfh.us* to send a message to world leaders that our future is not just about some of us, but all of us.

# About the Author

## His Unique Perspective

After the terrorist attacks of 9/11, John Moser became disillusioned with current political structures, fearing that too little cooperation and communication among world leaders was dooming us all. Moser feels that while there was horrible loss of life directly from 9/11, its indirect effects are the real problem. It is the emotional reaction to these events and not the actual events themselves that makes the twenty-first century so dangerous. He refers to the post-9/11 culture as the last of three major biosociophysical eras: the Era of Human Versus Human. During this era, we have placed ourselves in a difficult predicament unique in the history of humanity: we are vastly more interconnected, face a declining resource base, and are in the midst of a huge and growing disparity in wealth. These conditions are a perfect storm that place us at risk for a self-perpetuated die-off.

While Moser has no formal diplomatic experience, he has a unique perspective to offer diplomats—and the population in general—throughout the world: the current system of nation-states is broken and must be fixed before a major die-off occurs. The illusion is that we think we are better off then we have ever been because our attempts to fend off the natural environment have been so successful. The reality, however, is that our social environment has become light years more complex and intransigent to problem solving. We know the answers to our problems but never truly solve them; instead we create pseudo-solutions to placate vested interests. Nowhere is this more evident than in the medical system of the United States, something Moser knows plenty about.

His unique perspective as an experienced physician working within the medical establishment for the past 20 years has given him a fresh, critical perspective on our social environment today. He argues that the world's problem solving, as is the case with the health care system, centers on helping people with power and not necessarily humanity. The huge amounts of money spent on our health care system, for example, really do little to help humanity in general, but merely line the wallets of those in the medical-industrial complex. As an example, he cites the unfortunate relationship of tobacco to health care. It has been more than 60 years since we discovered the irrefutable harm that tobacco does, yet we still see hundreds of thousands of deaths annually and no ban against its use today. If anything, tobacco use is increasing throughout the world, as an oblivious Supercivilization fails to seriously consider real solutions. Social—not natural—problems are the inevitable obstacle of our Supercivilization, giving us little hope for resolution in the obsolete twentieth century paradigm permanently implanted in our leaders' minds today.

Moser now fears that what has happened in health care is happening to all types of problems for humanity. Climate change, illegal immigration, terrorism, and drug abuse are a few of the problems that will never be resolved unless and until we truly embrace the real solutions for humanity. Moser asks the question: do we want to save individual humans or do we want to save humanity? If the former is the case, then welcome to a die-off. If we choose the latter, then there is hope. After studying these topics for the last twelve years, Moser is convinced that until we have representation through enfranchisement for all of humanity and not just the most fortunate humans, problem solving will be difficult, if not impossible.

## HIS MOTIVATION

After researching for a bioterrorism lecture he gave to physicians in Fresno, California, in December 2001, he set a goal for persuading humanity in general to think in terms of a new twenty-first century paradigm: the notion of a Supercivilization. Over the course of the last twelve years he carefully reviewed thousands of documents. Given his experience as a doctor, he noted several failing parallels between terrorism, climate change, and extraordinary rises in health care costs: the dawning of modern humans. The development of modern humans, unlike any other previous time, is now faced with mandatory socialization. Because patients and doctors "need" the health care system and because our health care system has created its own monopoly by convincing people to conceive of their health through a disease model, our health care system has ascended the throne in successfully mastering our psyche. We see no other way but to capitulate. We have created an animate world of vested interests who think about themselves first and humanity second. In previous eras, this type of egotism was good, but unfortunately in an era with profound interconnectedness and resource depletion, egotism is now counterproductive.

Rationing for the general good must now take place, and that is impossible given our current nation-state paradigm offering insufficient oversight of humanity. The closest institution we have to a safeguard for humanity, the United Nations, is plagued with weak leadership and a functional mission statement biased toward the good of a minority of human beings: the wealthiest members of the wealthiest countries. By creating a stronger centralized government for humanity, we enfranchise all individuals throughout the world and begin to solve problems in a way that will truly benefit everyone. Until that happens, the small, wealthy minority who believed until the twenty-first century that they would benefit from pseudosolutions (and who assumed the rest of humanity would eventually benefit through a trickle-down effect) will suffer losses in the die-off along with the rest of us. The problems of the twenty-first century are far too big for any single individual, class, or country to resolve. Total, 100 percent consensus is now needed to resolve the major problems of the Supercivilization.

## HIS BACKGROUND

Dr. Moser has had an eclectic background. He graduated with a bachelor's degree in sociology from the University of California, Berkeley, in 1985. For three years he was involved in psychiatric care of children at Napa State Hospital. He also worked in a chemistry laboratory analyzing the geothermal geysers of Mendocino and Sonoma counties. He graduated from Tufts University School of Medicine in 1992 and completed his residency in emergency medicine at the Fresno campus of the University of California, San Francisco. He received the honors of chief resident and was a member of the clinical faculty at UCSF from 1996 to 2004. Between 1999 and 2004 he was quality assurance director of the emergency department at Community Hospitals in Fresno, California. He currently works in the emergency department at Sutter General Hospital in Sacramento, California.

Moser is the founder and CEO of Humans for a Healthier World, a nonprofit that seeks to educate and motivate individuals to form a consensus on world problems. He feels there is a need to give individuals a twenty-first century perspective that is not being presented through our current media. Giving individuals a perspective on global cooperation and eliminating unmitigated, unrestricted competition are the major goals of this organization. Moser and his organization strongly support discussions about stronger global governance, perhaps even an overarching global government in the ultimate hope of seeing a 100 percent consensus on problems such as world poverty, climate change, world health problems, and terrorism. In forming this organization, his main concern has been the potential for a human die-off of monumental proportions because of the unyielding resolve of current politicians to address their own constituents' concerns rather than humanitarian concerns. Currently working with pre-medical students, Moser sees hope. Ideas to spawn more effective solutions often come from the younger members of society who are not vested in longstanding paradigms that often discourage more effective solutions. His organization can be visited online at www.healthierworld.us and can be reached at info@healthierworld.us.

# ABOUT HUMANS FOR A HEALTHIER WORLD

Humans for a Healthier World is an organization promoting the Mission Statement for Humanity (see introduction). By promoting this mission statement, we hope to avoid serious resource declines, promote better standards of living, and mitigate and even eliminate the possibility of a self-induced annihilation throughout the world. Humanity has never faced a more critical time because of the *real* possibility of self-annihilation, and we need to create unprecedented cooperation to give ourselves a chance. We fear that the twenty-first century could be humanity's last. Our goal is to have all seven billion people in the world sign the Mission Statement.

Based upon the theoretical principles laid out in this book, Humans for a Healthier World's goal is to promote all ten points in the Mission Statement. Humans for a Healthier World welcomes new members at www.healthierworld. us or 855-864-2040. We are based in Napa Valley, California, USA, and we welcome all seven billion members of the Supercivilization to join us in our quest.

John Moser started this project in 2001 after 9/11 and has been working on the foundation for the Mission Statement and his book for the past 12 years. His motives were an outgrowth of the poor handling of 9/11 and of two wars spent "getting back at" terrorists. Moser feels that terrorism is a symptom of a much larger problem: the sociologically modern world in which we have too much interconnectedness, too few resources, and too much disparity in wealth. Can we navigate a course through the twenty-first century without a major die-off? Moser is not optimistic but feels the fundamental changes must be sociological in nature and so far the changes are insufficient to really give humanity a chance at self-survival. Until we develop newer, more fundamentally effective global institutions, such as a more effective global government, humanity will be at great risk for suicide.